HEADMAN

by KIN PLATT

HEADMAN

GREENWILLOW BOOKS
A Division of William Morrow & Company, Inc.
New York

Library of Congress Cataloging in Publication Data

Platt, Kin. Headman.
Summary: A teenage boy tries to find a way of
surviving in his bleak and violent city neighborhood.
[1. Juvenile delinquency—Fiction] I. Title.
PZ7.P7125He [Fic] 75-11808 ISBN 0-688-80011-4
ISBN 0-688-84011-6 (lib. bdg.)

HEADMAN

1

The silent fear came on slowly. Then it was rooted and part of him. The sun was blazing. Heat from the pavement sucked at his feet. Sweat crawled along his neck. The street was wide and empty but he needed more room. He lengthened his stride. The following footsteps shuffled relentlessly behind him.

The neighborhood looked deserted. A plague had wasted the inhabitants. Motionless cars without drivers stood gleaming at the curb ahead. The air was still. Tall grimed office buildings lined the street silently.

Jesus! Where the hell is everybody?

The corner was miles away and then he caught up to it and turned. He walked faster, listening. A store featured electric appliances and he made himself turn and look into the window. He yawned. Then they came around the corner in no particular hurry.

There were three of them.

He wasn't familiar with the gangs in this neighborhood. It wasn't very healthy to walk strange turf. This could be one hell of a problem.

Stupid jerk, he told himself.

1

The boys stalking him could be the Huns, or the Mumms. Maybe the Fourth Streeters.

Jerk, wake up, did we pass Fourth Street?

He walked, eyes rolling like marbles in his head, seeking escape. Down the long street ahead past the silent office buildings were old factories. Most of the windows were gaping holes or splintered glass. Closed down. Condemned. Nobody working. Downtown East Los Angeles abandoned, up for sale, shit.

He couldn't see any kids playing anywhere, no cats, no dogs. No people moving, no cars he could run to for help.

Jesus, this is really some kind of asshole neighborhood you got yourself stuck in, jerk!

A soft sigh escaped him when he saw the open alley across the street. About a hundred yards away and it had to be his only chance. Alleys had back fences with houses and backyards beyond. Over the fence he could find cover, double back, find his way out of this asshole neighborhood.

He didn't have to think twice about it. He shrugged his shoulders loose, sucked in a quick breath.

All right, man—let's go!

His arms and legs were pistons. Behind him sounded a loud shout. His sudden move had surprised them.

Tough shit, man.

Head lowered, he raced for the alley opening. The air flowed warmly past his face. He was inside the vacuum making things happen. He heard them come yelling after him.

2

No way, he thought, exultant in his terror. He was too fast for these cats. He was faster than anybody.

He rocketed into the long dark alley. The walls were piss-stained green. The slapping sound of his feet echoed around him sharp as pistol shots. His heart pounded.

Come on, you mothers. Catch me.

The factory walls framing the alley passage blurred. Head-high graffiti in thick black flowing strokes. *Mary sucks. Huns is shit. Mumms is boss.* The yelling noise behind him bounced off the high brick walls. Fainter now. He was losing them.

He couldn't believe the high solid stone wall at the end. It loomed upon him suddenly out of the darkness.

Shit, man. Dead end.

He ran into it just the same. Kicked at it, attacked it with his hands. *Goddamn wall. What asshole put it here?* His heart hammered pompompompompomp. The terror came up acrid and bile-sour, tightening his throat. Somehow lead seeped into his legs. Something screamed inside him.

They came into the alley behind him.

Son of a bitch goddamn fucking asshole wall you shit.

He turned around unwillingly. He didn't like what was happening to him inside. His chest hurt. Crawling goose-flesh ice prickled his arms.

Oh, shit, come on, he told himself. *Stay loose. It ain't the end of the world. Don't fold on me for Crissakes. It's only three guys.*

3

There was a side-door entrance to the old factory on his left. The dull gleaming brass knob turned in his hand. The lock held. The metal door was green-painted. He hit it hard with his shoulder, hoping for the best anyway.

No way. That mother is locked up tight.

They were well inside the alley, wide apart to cover him when he came. He stepped sideways to the other factory door. It held against his weight and fear. He sagged dead-spirited against it for a moment. They came on, moving in no hurry and without any noise.

He pushed away from the metal door to face them.

Behind him now was the high stone concrete wall forming a tight T between the old factory buildings. Some fucking alley this was. If he had wings, he could fly over that big mother wall.

But he didn't have wings and if he let them come at him, they would beat him against that back wall at the end of the alley. Beat and stomp him to a pulp with nobody around to break it up.

He hated the high wall now insanely. *Goddamn motherfucking wall faked me out.*

Up front is where it's at now, he told himself. *Up toward the street. Back here you're dead.*

He moved up.

Their upper bodies swayed, feinting him on. Showing him the alley opening. Taking it away. All he had to do was run through them. Their grins mocked his doing it.

Twenty feet away he checked them out. The middle

4

dude wore a white T-shirt. The paddy on the left a green crew neck. Red sport shirt for the third. They wore blue jeans, soiled and faded. They weren't especially ugly. They could have been anybody his age. Maybe a little older, sixteen, seventeen. Three on one was what made it the problem.

He kept moving side to side, taking them with him. *No way I'm going through till I know what these mothers fixing to lay on me.*

Green crew neck looked the youngest. Dark eyes. Brown hair. Acne pitted his moon face. He came dancing in first, making a short breathy sound from the top of his chest.

Hup hup hup hup.

Maybe his old man was in the army. What's he got there?

It flowed out of his hand then, jangling metal links. *Tire chain. Ain't that nice!*

He feinted right, stepped left out of range. Their feet were busy. Shoe leather creaked. Nails in their thick heels scraped the concrete. Black stomping boots.

The stocky one in the center came up to close the gap. *Man, he's bigger than I thought.* His barrel chest filled the white T-shirt. Thick round arms. Big hands weaving together now in a dull slapping sound.

Owen shifted carefully watching the light-haired boy in the T-shirt. Pale blue eyes with no light in them. T-shirt's hands parted and he came in with his right high and forward.

Oh, ain't this great! This cat ain't only big enough to

5

break me in half without trying. He has to have a tire iron. Jesus!

He felt the wall behind him and edged off. The only good thing about that mother wall was if he stayed close, they couldn't get behind him. But if they decided to rush him, they could pin him up against it. Hammer him down.

He shook his head. *Forget the fucking wall.*

There was still the other in the red shirt. *What's he carrying?*

This one was tall and thin. Frail looking. His long thin face was freckled, red hair curling below his ears. He came dancing in high on his toes. Elbows high, hunched shoulders, beating his fists together.

I don't see nothing. Maybe this mother's a good street fighter.

The redhead grinned. One hand disappeared behind him and he brought it back and snapped his wrist.

T-sing!

Jesus! He's got a blade.

He rolled away, his heart beating so loudly he felt sure they could hear it. *Ain't no way out now*, he told himself.

Hot anger controlled his terror. Three on one and they all had good weapons. *Well, shee-it!* He twisted away and reached back into his hip pocket. He felt the smooth hard bone handle. *This ain't no game now.* He brought it out in a flowing motion he had rehearsed thousands of times. He pressed the release spring and whipped his wrist out in a quick downward arc.

6

The steel blade vibrated in its own sound.

Okay? You all see it? Right on. Now we all know what we got.

They backed off and gave him space in the alley. If he wanted to, he could attack, surprise them, drive them back.

Then what? he thought bleakly. He remembered other fights.

They were moving in again. He'd blown his chance. A harsh rasping sound worried him. Is that coming from me? he wondered. It came closer, enveloping him. He became part of it and then he knew. It wasn't just him.

Everybody was nervous.

There was a sudden sharp explosive noise and he froze, quivering. *Oh, come on. It's only a truck backfiring out there. Nobody's shooting at nobody. Come on. Pay attention.*

They were shuffling in, gliding back, feinting with hands and shoulders, menacing with their weapons. He was wearing down. Too uptight now. The voice was his but he didn't recognize it at first. *What's happening?*

"Okay, you mothers. Who wants it first?" He stared down the length of his arm and saw his blade jabbing at the air. *Okay, so you told them. I don't see nobody running.*

The weaving line flowed back to him now. The dude in the T-shirt came in crabwise like a fencer. Right foot out, sliding under the right arm. *Watch that fucking tire iron,* he told himself. The others took back the space they had allowed him. They were close enough to hurt him.

Hup hup hup. The tire chain kid came angling in. He remembered he had to watch the knife. The long arm of the redhead wigwagged in a wide sweeping motion. The knife blade glinted in the air and he took a step off the line. The tire chain was a quick blur in the air. He knew he was late when he raised his left arm to block it off. The blow was glancing. His arm went numb and then the fire of pain began. *Jesus! What the fuck?*

The silent inner voice he could never escape mocked him. *Good move there, Owen baby. Couple more like that you'll wish you was dead.*

They came at him again driving him back. He gave too much attention to the swish of the heavy chain now. He never saw the tire iron snaking in to his side. He bit his lip at the impact, feeling his body shudder and recoil from the stabbing deep pain.

They'd had him twice now and he couldn't keep taking the blows. Desperation and pain made him move and put it together. He darted in low, weaving fighter style, and then jabbed straight out. The knife thrust struck home. He felt it in his fingers past the ripping skin when it reached the bone.

The husky blond kid cursed. The tire iron clanged to the alley pavement. He clapped a hand over his forearm. Blood dripped darkly between his fingers.

The tire chain caught him again. Low on his leg and he gasped at the pain. *Jesus! They'll chop you to rib-*

8

bons, he said to himself, and somehow he was charging out of the pocket, lashing with his blade. He caught the boy with the chain against the factory wall and punched hard with the blade.

The boy screamed and his head fell back. His eyes rolled in his head and he clutched at his body as if trying to hold it together. *Maybe now's the time,* Owen thought. He feinted at the redhead driving him back and showed him the bloody blade again before he turned and ran for the alley opening.

The husky kid wearing the T-shirt was hurt, and stepped out of his way. He fell to the pavement and Owen said, "Yeah!" and darted between him and the building wall.

He was just beginning to find his stride, the street clearly ahead, when something heavy clanged off the wall. His head went numb and his legs buckled. As he was falling, he was telling himself, *Goddamn tire iron! I told you to watch it!*

There were muffled sounds that hurt. His eyes flicked open and they were over him from all sides, kicking, trying to stomp him out. A heavy blow to his ribs took his breath away. His limp body shuddered, helpless under the attack.

His mind nagged at him. *Nobody can live with this. You better do something. Get up, they're killing us.*

The heavy boot heels stomped his chest. Somehow he rolled over. His hand found his knife and he thrust his arm up savagely. Somebody screamed.

He was swaying on his knees, trying to shield his

9

head. A heavy blow rocked him and he struck out again. A thin voice cried out and cursed him. It was raining soft and sticky.

He heard running feet and suddenly nobody was beating at him. A siren wailed in the distance.

He pulled himself up holding the brick wall. A red stain covered his hands. His head felt lopsided. Pain stabbed deep inside when he tried to take a breath. The buildings tilted. The street went up and down. *Jesus!*

His own blood was strangling him. He choked, retched, jackknifed over and tried to spit. His lips were mashed raw. He turned his head at a whimpering sound.

The husky blond lay on the ground. The white T-shirt was turning red. Owen pushed his tongue against swollen lips. *Well, what the fuck you expect?*

He saw the redhead sagging back against the brick wall. He was crying. His thin chest heaved and jerked. His red shirt was splotched with a deeper, darker red. A dark reddening stain covered one leg of his blue jeans.

The siren wailed closer and stopped. He tried to clear his head. He shook it and blood sprayed in a fine mist. *I better get outta here*, he told himself. He took two steps.

He looked up surprised at two policemen. They were propping him up to a sitting position. He wondered, Where they come from?

"Christ!" one of them said. "What in the hell happened here?"

10

I got myself messed, Owen wanted to say, it's the curse of the Kirbys. But he didn't have enough left to say anything. It was easier to let his eyes close and float down the long slide into the dark bottomless pit where suddenly it was very peaceful and quiet and he didn't feel a thing.

The big bus stank. It looked like a Greyhound intercity but the black letters outside read Los Angeles County Sheriff's Department. It had left the city and was grinding and bouncing north along Highway 101. Coastline hills on the right were smooth and golden. He saw stone castles on solitary bluffs. The Pacific blurred green and deep blue out the left-side windows as far as he could see.

I finally saw my first ocean.

Outside the bus was painted black and white. The two rear windows were barred. Heavy wire mesh screened all the side windows. There were two guards armed with holstered revolvers.

Owen dozed fitfully. He shifted his sore backside on the hot cracked worn leather. His seat companion jerked protestingly in his sleep.

Can't help it, Jack, Owen said silently. *They fit you so tight in here, ain't room to move your ass.*

There were thirty boys aboard. Young juvenile offenders ranging in age from eleven to seventeen. Black, white, red and brown. The California Youth Authority handled all colors.

The guard sitting up front was black. He had the

12

pump seat facing them. The one in the rear was white. They were big men sitting relaxed, expressionless. McKeon, the man from the juvenile probation department, sat behind the bus driver opposite the front door.

McKeon was sandy-haired with a ruddy complexion. Deep-chested with wide sloping shoulders. He looked like a heavyweight fighter gone into middle-age flab. His nose was dented, flattened at the bridge. His eyes were ice blue and hard. He was pleasant-faced. His light tan suit was rumpled as he perspired in the late morning heat. His thick hands covered with light wiry hair dangled limply across his paunch.

Owen watched him. *You don't fuck around none with this cat.*

He tried to fix on McKeon's eyes, catch his look and stare him down. But the big man sat placidly slumped in his seat, hard eyes squinting against the sun. The bus jolted and his bulky body bounced on the hard seat. His eyes shifted, quartering the busload of boys. His piercing gaze held briefly on Owen, flicked and passed on.

Anyway he noticed me. He saw I ain't afraid.

The long bus ride began in a chill morning drizzle at Juvenile Hall in downtown Los Angeles. The driver was cheerful. "Morning, boys. Welcome aboard. Take any seats you want. It's all free and paid for."

A few answered him. "Ain't that nice! What time we comin' back?"

"Hey, we goin' to Disneyland?"

"Jesus, this bus stinks! Smell those seats!"

"It ain't a bus, *amigo*—it's a cattle car."

McKeon and the guards came on next. McKeon listened to the bitching and griping, smiling steadily, helped them get seated. "It'll be a long ride, boys. Make yourselves comfortable."

"How we gonna do that, man? I'm uncomfortable already."

The driver closed the doors, honked his horn and pulled into the street traffic. Morning traffic was heavy and the bus ground along slowly through the rain. By the time they hit the freeways girdling the downtown area, the interior of the bus was hot and stuffy.

The rain eased and the bus ground alongside freeway traffic, making better time. Owen sat next to the window, ignoring his seating companion, trying to stare through the sweating wet glass.

When they reached the Pacific coastal highway, the sun came out. Somebody in the back cheered. The broad highway at times ran close to the ocean. Long green rolling waves came tumbling onto the wet sand.

Man, that looks cold, he thought.

The window cleared and he could see surfers riding the long curling waves.

Craggy rain-fissured cliffs blocked out the beaches. Farther north at Malibu and Point Mugu the surfers reappeared. Sitting astride their boards, paddling with their hands out to sea. Waiting for their waves. Coming in scrambling on long finned boards. Walking along shifting their weight. Fighting for balance. Plowing

14

through under the running trough of the curling waves. Riding the tube.

Lank-haired sun-bronzed boys. Shapely long-haired blonde bikini girls. Laughing. Playing games.

It didn't seem real. Nobody to hassle you. Just get on your fucking board and go. Jesus!

The juvenile offenders stared out the steamed windows, fascinated. They cheered whenever a surfer went down.

"Stay down, creep! Take a count!"

"Look out, ya jerk! Aaaah! I told ya!"

"Aw, I can do that, too, only my bathtub ain't big enough."

"Hey, will ya look at the boobs on that one!"

"The one in pink?"

"No, the one in white. Hey, wait—the pink ain't bad."

"Hey, driver—lemme out. I gotta pee."

Owen heard it all and remained silent.

Anyway, if you never see it again, you saw it.

Maybe you ought to try that sometime, he said to himself. That crap looks neat.

Jesus, you for real? Me on one of them fuckers.

The CYA bus veered inland away from the water. The gibes and cheers of the passengers changed to groans.

"Hey, man, where ya goin'?"

"Yeah, somebody shoot the driver. He's lost."

"Back up, man. We just blew the ocean."

McKeon shook his head, smiling sympathetically. The guards were smiling, too.

15

Owen slumped in his seat. *Yeah, that's the way they do you. Show you something nice, then take it away. Next time I ain't even looking.*

The new freeway unraveled glaringly before them, a bright winding ribbon between green mountains. There was an occasional house set off the road or nestled in the hills. But mostly the landscape was groves of trees and mile after mile of bare yellowed grass.

Jesus! Lookit all that space! Nobody lives here!

The bus picked up speed, running smoothly now, and he nodded. Yeah, he said silently. Let's get it over with fast. This ain't supposed to be no pleasure trip.

Then he thought, I wonder what it's gonna be like, and his mind switched back automatically to the big room in Juvenile Hall.

He was standing behind a wooden railing, looking up at a black-robed old man, feeling cold and nervous.

The old man read from the sheet of paper. "Robbery . . . possession of firearms . . . assault . . . auto theft . . . trespassing and refusal to move on . . . larceny . . . attempting to sell stolen property . . . assault with dangerous weapon. . . ."

Well, sure, he wanted to say, but everybody does that jazz. All the kids. That's how we do on the street, man.

He stood locked in worry. He had given his word to the young public defender. Bright guy. Wavy black hair. Thin hatchet face. Alert eyes. "Just keep your lip buttoned up, kid. Don't answer back. Don't interrupt. They don't like smart-ass kids here. Okay?"

"Okay."

"Because if you're a smart-ass, you can wind up doing hard time. You know what that's like?"

"Yeah."

"Another thing. Where's your mother? Can't she come down here?"

Yeah, sure, if she was sober enough, man.

"She's sick," he said. "She can't make it."

"What about your father?"

"He copped out. Left a long time ago." He nodded to the papers from the psychiatric social workers. "It's down there."

"Oh. Yes. Hmm. Too bad."

"It's okay. Nobody misses him."

Jesus, all those questions. They knew more about him than he did. The tests to understand his problems. His home life. Kind of crappy, he told them.

Nobody was surprised. There were lots worse off. But it would all go to the court and to the probation officer, they told him, and then it was up to the referee or judge at Juvenile Court. It would be a comprehensive evaluation, they said, with their recommendations.

He had to guess what it meant. Words bugged him. Fuck it, he told himself. It always came back to that anyway.

There were two flags on the wall behind the judge and the clerk. The California bear flag. The one of the United States. He heard the people on the judge's side whispering. There was nothing on his record to show he had ever been on probation or served time.

I ain't the only one. There's lots worse than me.

17

A child cried behind him. A burly sheriff's deputy came across the crowded room to shut up the kid. The judge and the public defender were talking. The eager-beaver defender was smiling. The old man sat back, tossing papers down. The defending attorney beckoned Owen, put a hand on his shoulder. "The judge accepted our plea of self-defense. You're getting a break, boy. Only two years at the youth camp and a chance of parole within a year with good behavior. You should thank him."

Two years? Man, you're talking like it was two weeks!

"It's a camp, not a prison, Owen. It doesn't go on your record, you see. You'll still be eligible to vote and hold office when you're old enough." The defender gripped his arm.

Owen's eyes turned inward. *Hold office? Who, me? Man, you're far out!* Aloud he said, "Yeah. Okay. Sure."

The judge didn't look up or respond when he stepped forward. He was glancing over a sheaf of paper listing the record of the next juvenile offender. He was shaking his head, moving his lips, not saying anything. His gray eyes looked troubled.

Owen shrugged. *Okay, man—where's the handcuffs?*

The young defender had his arm again. Pulling him away. "You're getting a break, kid. Behave yourself. Fly right now. Understand?"

He looked over his shoulder. He didn't see the three boys who had cornered and stomped him.

"What's the name of the place? You know—the camp?"

"I don't know, kid. What's the difference? You bought

18

it for yourself, right? Excuse me, now—I got this other boy to look after."

The bus jolted. He opened his eyes and saw they had stopped. McKeon, the man from probation, was on his feet. "Let's go, boys. This is it."

He looked out the bus window. There was a cluster of low buildings in a clearing surrounded by tall pines. A wooden gate stood open and a narrow dirt road ran through. A weather-beaten wooden sign hung over the gatepost.

He read it twice.

Camp Sawyer.

Two years, he thought. Two fucking years! *Jesus, you ready for this?*

3

He lay on his bunk staring upward.

There were three blacks in the small cottage. Three whites. Three Chicano Mexican-Americans. The floors were scrubbed clean, walls freshly painted. The bedding on the narrow cots smelled fresh. The pillow cases were crisp and clean.

Man, this is better than home.

He thought about Adams, the camp director.

They had shuffled unwillingly into three long lines as McKeon called their names from a list. "Chickenshit," a tall black boy muttered. McKeon kept on calling names briskly.

A door swung open from the nearest cottage. A man came toward them. "Welcome to Camp Sawyer, boys." His tanned face was seamed with tiny wrinkles that rolled into place when he smiled.

He stood aside smiling until McKeon was through and the three lines were formed. McKeon handed him the paper list.

Now what? Owen thought. Who's this dude?

He folded the paper into his pocket, smiled into their

expressionless hostile faces. "My name is Adams, fellows," he said quietly. "I'm the probation director up here, and the person you want to talk to if you have any problems."

They stared sullenly.

Adams smiled. His eyes shifted down the lines as if moving to encompass them all. "You can expect some difficulties at first but don't let it throw you. We don't expect things to go right all at once. Our aim here is to do all we can to help you boys get yourselves together, so that when you leave you can try for a better life."

Yeah. Only how we gonna do that, man?

Adams nodded encouragingly. "After we find bunks for everybody, and get you all sorted out, we'll have some chow. Then we'll rap a little about what it's going to be like up here. Camp Sawyer isn't a rest camp and it isn't a jail. We hope it's what you all want it to be. Something special."

Bullshit, Owen thought. How can it be good? With these mothers? Look at them cats, man. They'd as soon cut you up as look at you.

Adams said, "I can guess what you're thinking. What's this dude laying on us? We all did a lot of things on the street to get into trouble. We've been fooled before. We don't expect anything special."

The boys looked at Adams as if he weren't there. They shuffled their feet. They scratched, yawned. They were beat from the long hot bus ride, and hungry. One thing we don't want now, Owen wanted to tell the man,

21

is more bullshit. Maybe later but not now. *You're wasting it now, man.*

Adams held his smile, nodding pleasantly. He turned to McKeon. "A lot of boys have been through here and we're proud of them. Isn't that so, Mr. McKeon?"

McKeon rubbed his jaw. He looked them over casually, without rancor. His voice was flat, impersonal. "Some do okay."

Owen marked him mentally. *He don't bullshit for nobody.*

Adams raised his hand and turned. "All right, boys. If you'll come this way, please."

He and McKeon headed toward the far end of a group of low cottages. The single-file lines dissolved into a group of stragglers falling in behind. From the far end of the camp, they heard shouts and laughter.

Behind the tall stand of pines, the distant hills were flooded with a deepening purple as the sky darkened abruptly.

"Hey, man—where the street lights?"

"They took 'em away along with the streets."

A boy sniffed at the crisp fresh evening. "Hey, get a whiff of that, man. Is that air?"

"That ain't air, man. That's chickenshit. We're gonna get plenty of that here. They gonna talk us to death."

Don't think about nothing, he told himself. *Stay loose.*

Later, after they had eaten, Adams spoke to them in the cafeteria. He watched as the first defiant ones openly struck up matches to cigarettes. "Smoke if you

22

want to. We don't have too many rules to bug you."
He went on to tell them that Camp Sawyer hopefully
could be the turning point of their lives. It didn't matter
what they had been or had done. Here was where everything would change. Here was where a kid in trouble
could get a new start.

"Don't ask me how," he added. "I'm not a magician.
I'm only here to help. The rest will be up to you boys."

Yeah. Sure. You bet.

He could guess the expressions on the faces of the
boys around him without having to look. He looked
anyway.

Yeah. Rotsa ruck there, Adams.

Lights went out at nine. He could hear the sounds
of the others in the room sleeping. He didn't think he
was sleepy. *Nine o'clock? Who goes to bed at nine
o'clock?*

At Juvenile Hall, if you knew what was good for you,
you didn't go to sleep at nine o'clock. If you were wise,
you didn't go to sleep at all.

He had found out the first night when a big black
dude had squeezed his ass. "You gonna be my sweetie
tonight."

"Yeah? You try something, I'll call the guard."

Soft laughter. "He won't do you any better, man."

He knew what to expect at Juvenile Hall. There were
over 500 young delinquents in there ranging in age from
ten to eighteen. Boys and girls in trouble. Black, brown,
yellow, red and white. Hub-cap lifters, runaways, mug-

23

gers, dope addicts, psychos and attempted murderers.

Juvenile Hall was gang-dominated. The bloods ran it. Outside, they were hounded. Inside the power roles were reversed.

The lucky ones got to sleep in a cell-like cage. No plumbing. Heavily screened walls and windows. They were locked in at night and the gangs couldn't get at them.

The others slept on thin mattresses on the floor. Owen didn't sleep for several nights. Instead he dozed during the long interminable days.

He noticed the Chicanos were let alone because they stuck together in protective units. If one of them got messed by a blood or paddy, the Chicano gang fought back.

I got to get me a gang, Owen thought. You need protection.

There was scuttlebutt about the food. The word was out that the boys who worked in the kitchen spit and urinated in the food. The rumor was they did it to get even. They didn't like the hall or what was happening to them. They did it to get their own back on the gangs who bullied them.

There was talk about gang rape. One of their members decoyed the guard. The rest came in with a sheet or blanket to cover their victim. They would force him into one of the sleeping rooms, rape him under a cot, or in a dark bathroom.

Owen shuddered. *Jesus! Maybe it could happen here!*

24

He sat up cautiously. His eyes adjusted to the darkness. He looked into the farthest corners. He listened hard but all he could hear was his own thumping heart and the sleeping sounds of his roommates.

Maybe when you get to know them better, it will be okay, he told himself.

Yeah. Fat chance.

He lay back, hands locked behind his head, wondering what it was going to be like at Camp Sawyer. Jesus, he didn't even know where it was. Upstate somewhere. Someplace in the country. He didn't hear any traffic. The air smelled clean.

Adams had said here was where everything would change.

How'm I gonna change? he wondered.

He wondered if his old man had ever spent time in a youth correction camp. *Maybe I got it from him.*

Okay, Pops. Here I am. Your favorite son. You wanna lay some words advice on me?

He wondered if they told his old lady, how she took the news. *She probably don't even notice I'm gone.*

When I get outta this dumb camp, he told himself, I'll show her. I'll be somebody.

Yeah? Like what?

He tried reaching out in his mind to grasp the future. The picture was blank. Nothing there at all but space. Then he saw himself running across the picture. Breathing hard. Scared.

For his life? he wondered. *Jesus, always?*

He thought about the other kids next to him and across the room. He didn't know any of them but he knew others a lot like them.

Running with gangs. Stealing. Fighting. Stabbing. Shooting.

They all got to wind up in the clink, he told himself.

What about yourself? What plans you got to be a big man?

I don't know yet, he told his inner mocking voice. *Gimme time. Don't bug me.*

A boy across the room suddenly yelled in his sleep. "Don't hit me! Don't hit me, you mother!" He thrashed wildly in his covers and then muttered off into sleep again.

Owen shivered. He drew the sheet and blanket high over his face. Then he was asleep. In his dream, people were yelling at him, hemming him inside a tight circle, and he couldn't break out. Then they were hitting him and he heard himself yelling and screaming.

He fought back against a solid wall of flesh. He was punching hard but his blows seemed to have no effect. They were laughing at him. Then they were dragging him down and he heard more yelling, but it didn't seem to be coming from him. He heard a shrill whistle, running feet, more yelling.

Hey, cut out that yelling, he wanted to say. Man, you're hurting my ears.

He felt himself being grabbed and shaken and he started up angrily. He was surprised to see he was awake. A dark face was close to his, smiling.

"Man, you sleep like you're dead. I've been blowing my whistle right in your ears!"

He blinked, sat up groggily. "Huh?"

"You're Kirby, aren't you? Fall out, man. We got to start your first day at Camp Sawyer right. Let's go!"

Owen frowned. *Who was this dude?* He saw the others on their feet, getting dressed in the cold dark room. Bitching about it. Cursing. "Jesus, my ass is freezing!"

He groaned and started to fall back. "It's still night, man. Who says we got to get up?"

"I do. I'm Johnson, your group leader. Chow's at six. If you miss it, you don't eat. You coming?"

He was surprised to see his feet already swinging over the side of his narrow bed.

Well, shit, we got to eat.

4 There were sixty boys at the camp now. McKeon had gone back to L.A., taking a bus load with him.

Two more years it'll be my turn.

He was sitting with Adams in the director's office. "You put in your time, they got to let you go—right?"

Adams didn't avoid his eyes. "That's the general idea. Sometimes a boy leaves sooner, if we all think he's ready." Adams fiddled with his pipe trying to get it to draw cleanly. "Sometimes he leaves, regardless."

What's that mean?

"How come, man?"

Adams jabbed his pipestem toward the window. "Look out there and tell me what you see."

"I see trees. What else? That what you want me to say?"

Adams grimaced. "I put it the wrong way. I should have asked what you don't see when you look outside."

Oh, man, this is getting heavy. What's he telling me?

He stared out the window, seeing nothing. *Trees, man. There's lots of trees out there. Only that ain't the answer.*

"Okay, I give up. What's the answer?"

Adams made his eyes look bright and friendly. "What

28

I'm trying to say is, there aren't any fences or walls here. No guards."

No guards is bullshit, he thought. They came up with us on the bus. They got off here when we did.

He looked past Adams at the framed pictures on the wall. Kids under the shining glass. Playing games. Baseball crap. Working in a field looking like they liked it. Jesus!

"So some boys just take off," Adams was saying. "We don't try to stop them by force."

"You just take off when you want, huh?"

His anger couldn't be held. "I saw guards, man."

Adams lit his pipe, running his match over the top of the bowl in a rotary motion. "Those guards had to come along to bring you fellows up here. It's county regulation."

Yeah? I don't know about that stuff.

His denim work shirt smelled clean. They had his size. The pants felt thin around the knees. Maybe the last kid did a lot of praying to get out.

"We're trying a different kind of youth camp here," Adams said. "The old system didn't work. The boys had the feeling they were in jail."

Well, yeah. I thought that was supposed to be the whole idea.

Beyond the trees, he could see bright yellow patches of grass and then cloud-covered hills in the distance. The high green mountains looked unreachable, miles away, leaning stiffly against the blue sky. *Man, all them fucking trees.*

29

Maybe I can run away and be a mountain man, he thought. *Only I'd need a rifle, I guess.* He remembered a movie about an old-time mountain man. Every step he took, there were these crazy Indians jumping him. The hero looked scared, he remembered, but he did all right, he still killed every one of them.

Oh, yeah, they killed his wife and kid, that's why.

I guess I could do that, he thought. If you're mad enough and you got the rifle, so you do it.

He remembered the spooky part where they rode their horses through the old Indian burial grounds. They weren't supposed to do that. It was sacred stuff. There was music and things moving and whispering and it was spooky as shit. But then they got it for what they did. Didn't the other guy get killed? Shit, yeah, and that's when the Indians ripped off his wife and kid, while they were being such assholes in the grave-yard.

Aloud he said, "You mean it ain't against the rules to just take off and split, if you feel like it?" That was crazy. *What kind of stupid system is that?*

We're all fuck-ups here, aren't we?

Adams said, "We know if a boy is unhappy here, he'll find a way to leave. We don't interfere. We try to do everything along the lines of the honor system."

The chair felt too hard. *Jesus, it's like sitting on a rock.* Smoke wreathed Adams's face. The tobacco smelled good. He thought maybe he ought to try a pipe some day.

They were always saying these things. Laying on the

30

heavy words he didn't understand. Come on, man, he wanted to say. Talk straight. What honor system? I mean, I don't know where the fuck that's at, man.

He sat slumped in the wooden chair looking down at his feet. The sneakers were a little too big. Maybe they were expecting him to grow into them. He moved his toes up and down.

"Okay," he said. Maybe Adams had to lay it on the line for every asshole to see which way they would jump. Maybe that's how they do here, he thought. "Okay. So what if I don't like the scene and I split? Like I cut out one day. Then suppose I get picked up some other place. Then what happens?"

Adams didn't look worried. Shit, it wasn't his ass, why should the man worry? *Look, the bastard's even smiling.* "If you get picked up," Adams said evenly, "they might send you to a place with tighter security next time. There are other camps."

He had heard about those. Places where they really whip your ass. He said, "Yeah. That figures."

Adams made sucking noises on his pipe. He couldn't pull any more smoke. The thing was dead. Adams tapped the pipe out on a big ash tray, then blew through the stem. He set the pipe down carefully upright against a thick book. "It would work against your chances of parole, for one thing, you know. It's all part of the record, you see."

Yeah, that figures, too.

Adams had a lot of papers on his desk. The man really had homework. He shuffled them around, fitting

31

some into a neat pile. "Sometimes a boy gets away with it," he said. "If he stays out of trouble, if he doesn't do anything foolish, he can get by for a while. It all depends, I guess, on what he's going to do with himself."

His own voice sounded thin and angry. "I got no place to go, man. If I go back, I'm on the street again. It's got to be trouble, man. I know it. It ain't worth it for the lousy two years. It ain't like I'm running numbers or like that. I got nothing going for me there. It would be the same hassle. Every day."

Adams bobbed his head, smiling. "Well, I wasn't encouraging your trying to run away. But a lot of boys wonder what's happening when they get here. We think we can help you fellows, if you give us a chance. That's our business, son."

It didn't pass. *Okay, so now I'm his son. Maybe I ought to call him Dad.*

Hey, Dad, what's happening?

"I ain't saying I won't cut out," he said. "Only this place will really have to do me before I split. It will really have to be bad, man. I mean *bad*. You know?"

Anyway, he thought, it's bad everywhere, so what's the difference? Except maybe if you own a surfboard and you got all that water and the long beach and those chicks.

Adams grinned and rubbed one side of his face. His skin was tan and leathery looking. He had about a million wrinkles when he smiled. Like his whole face was breaking up. He wanted to feel his own face.

I wonder when that happens? I mean, when you get

the crummy wrinkles. Man, I guess you got to be old.

"I don't think we're *that* bad," Adams said. He studied the paper in his hands. "Do you have any hobbies or special interests? Things you like to do?"

Well, yeah, man, like staying alive. I dig that.

The street came up plainly then inside his eyes. It had four corners on one end and four corners on the other. There was trouble waiting on any one of them. You could get yourself stomped or cut or killed by walking down the wrong street.

There ain't no exceptions to them rules, he thought. Only if you happen to be lucky that day.

He felt sick inside and despondent. When you were alone, you couldn't fight it. You just couldn't cut it on your own. I'm all I got, he thought, and it ain't too much.

He looked at Adams squarely. "I don't play no games, if that's what you mean. They sent me here to do my time, so I'll do it. I ain't copping no plea, man. I cut up some dudes because I had to. Maybe it'll happen again. If they don't get me one time, they get me the next. I don't care about doing the two-year stretch. It ain't nothing to me."

Something flared inside him. That secret part of himself that was always there watching, listening. *Hey, man,* it said, *what you saying? That's two years you are talking about. You know what that is? That's a lotta time, man. You want it, okay, but that don't mean we all got to like it.*

Owen grimaced, shaking his head. He waited to hear

33

if it had more to tell him. Man, he thought, what is that? Who is in charge here, anyway?

Adams shuffled papers. "It doesn't have to be the full two years. It's only a probation period. You might work your way out sooner. It depends. If you're ready, we'll let you know."

"We? Who's the *we?*"

"All of us here," Adams said. "The boys, the staff, me, you—but the boys themselves decide who can leave and when."

Man, that is more bullshit, he thought. Aloud, he said, "You're the headman. What if you don't like what's decided?"

Adams shrugged. "I'm not that important. I'm here to help you get yourselves together. I have to listen. But don't think it's that easy. There are sixty boys here at a given time. A majority has to be pulling for you to make it outside. They vote on you. You vote on them. We've found that to be a fair system, son."

Fair system? he thought. Man, I don't know no fair systems. It's all crap. I been screwed all my life. Everybody I know's been screwed. What the fuck you talking about, fair system? That's a crock.

He looked at Adams angrily, wanting to hit him.

"You mean, some cat don't like me, he can say 'Screw Kirby!' If he's got enough fink friends, they can hold me all they want."

"Well, yes, but it works the other way, too. You get enough of them on your side, and you won't have that problem."

34

*Shit I won't. I'm just me. I got no gang. So it's got
to be me against them. Like always.*

He was on his feet, hearing himself shouting. "Screw
them! I don't need no favors from nobody. Just lemme
alone. I'll do my time like I'm supposed."

Adams shrugged. He didn't appear disturbed. He
didn't look about to say, Sit down, punk, and listen, I
make the rules here.

Adams asked quietly, "How are you with a saw?"

"Huh? With a who?"

"We have over three hundred acres here. We've got
saws and axes for the boys who like cutting trees. Some
of it is farm. Maybe you might like that. Hogs and a
lot of chickens to feed. That's how we get our ham and
eggs."

Owen sat. "How do you mean?"

"We're all here to serve one another. That's the heart
of our program. The boys pick what kind of work they
prefer. There's carpentry work for those who want to
help build other cottages here. Laundry work. Cafeteria. There's also sweeping, dusting, mopping—keeping the place clean. We find boys are happier in a clean
place."

He scratched his head. "Jeez, I dunno. Do I have to
pick one now?"

"No. You'll fill out a work preference form soon."
Adams gathered the papers together and set them down
in a neat pile. "I've got a lot of other new boys to talk
to this morning. If you have any questions—?"

"That work jazz," he was saying cautiously. "I guess

that's for free, right? I mean, we don't get paid?"

"Well, it's not a heck of a lot, but yes, there is pay. We're not rich here and it all depends. Some you get to keep. Some you put back into the fund for entertainment. Some of the boys like to take short trips, vacations. That way, everybody chips in and everybody has fun." The man looked searchingly at Owen for the first time. "Have you ever had a real vacation, son?"

Owen was shaking his head. "No, sir. Man, this is my first one."

5 His body felt hard and strong. He wanted to run. Use his strength. Feel his muscles heat up. He was in the wrong gear for this place. Nothing to do and he would explode inside. He wished he understood what Adams was saying about work.

Johnson was waiting for him outside. Owen blinked in the dazzling sunlight. Cirrus clouds reached across the pale blue sky. The mountains looked very remote and restful.

"Which one you want, man?" Johnson said.

Johnson looked powerful. His black arm muscles glistened, rippled when he moved. His deep chest swelled under the white T-shirt. He was holding a tennis racket in one hand, a long-handled rake in the other.

Owen stopped short. "It's got to be one or the other, huh?"

"That's right."

One meant work in the yard. The other was games. It made no sense. Who wanted to work? "You mean, I get to play tennis whenever I want?"

Johnson wagged his head slowly side to side. "Who

said anything about when you want to? I'm talking about right now, Kirby. Which is it—the rake or the racket?"

He shrugged, feigning indifference. "I never took up tennis. And where I come from, we ain't got gardens. So I never used any of them mothers. Whatever you say, Johnson. I don't care which."

"You don't?"

"No, man. Whatever you say. That old man back in Juvenile Court didn't send me up here to play games, did he? I'm up here to get straightened out, right?"

Johnson dropped his hands. "Maybe you don't understand the whole bit, man. The Man sent you up because that's his job, see? His gig is administering the law. He sent you up because what else could he do, man? You didn't expect him to kiss you and put you back on the street?"

He had to smile. "Not too much."

"Damn right," Johnson said. "Okay. So he did his job and now up here we got to do ours. What we try to do is put you guys on to something that might set you straight. Some kids dig the tennis racket. It's something maybe they never did before and playing the game turns them on. Some other dudes, well maybe they don't want to play games and they dig hard work. Like using the rake, the shovel—that jazz. Some like working with their hands. We got machinery here—cars for them to fix. We got gardens—food to grow, in case you like the idea of making things happen."

Making things happen sounded good. He screwed his

eyes into the sun. The air smelled crisp and clean. On the ascending slopes before the mountains, the top branches of the tall pines and firs swayed with the breeze. The wind came in soft and easy. He wondered how long those trees had been there giving in to the wind.

Well, I ain't no tree, he told himself, but I'm here. I got to do something.

Johnson lifted his thick arms and swung them back. He inhaled deeply as if enjoying it. "Smell that air, Kirby. That's good for you. Good for your lungs. Coming from L.A. with all that garbage you got in the air, you got to appreciate this. It's part of the deal here. Good food, good healthy air. It's got to do something nice for your system."

He shrugged. "Yeah. The air's okay. It's sure different. It smells better anyway."

Johnson laughed. "Damn right. You smell garbage all the time, and all that poison, it's got to stink up your nose and sinuses. Infect your whole system."

"Yeah, I guess." He looked at the tennis racket and the rake again. Well, there they were in Johnson's big hands, in case he ever made up his mind.

Johnson breathed deeply and thumped his chest. "It's like taking a deep breath. You can expand up here. You can grow. Maybe you want to be a great artist. You don't know yet. Maybe you have things inside your head nobody knows about. We try to help you find it up here. We call it motivation."

He could feel the genuine warmth of Johnson reach-

39

ing out to him, coming to him like the wind. Only warmer, not trying to make him back up or knock him down. He wondered why Johnson was putting out for him when all these black dudes were up here.

His chin jerked toward the tennis racket. "Supposing I pick that mother? It takes two to play, don't it? Besides, I ain't sure I know which end to hold."

"Ain't that something?" Johnson said, and tossed Owen the racket. He reached out and saw the thick leather handle in his right hand.

"That's the right end," Johnson said. "Now, you want to learn how to hit a tennis ball with that mother?"

He made his jaw drop in mock surprise. "We get to use real tennis balls, too? Hey, man, what you running here—some kind of country club?"

Johnson grinned. "Man, you won't believe this, but after a time you'll be telling me you never had it so good. However, there is one thing I have to tell you. Just so it won't come as no big surprise. I mean, talking about this country club bit, you know?"

Over Johnson's head, the mountains glittered. No matter where he looked, the sun was bouncing off things, showing him a million lights. A bird called sharply behind his head and he heard the swift drumming of its wings. It swooped low behind the thick pines and called again.

He scuffed the ground with the toe of his sneaker. Well, you got to pay up, he told himself. One way or another, you got to pay. You ought to know that fresh air ain't free.

40

His voice mocked Johnson. "Come on, daddy-o. Tell me so I won't be surprised. I got nothing else to do but listen."

Johnson scowled. "It'll keep. Maybe I'm coming on too heavy." He dropped the long-handled rake. Behind him was a cardboard box. He picked it up and shook it. "Listen to that, man. You know what that is?"

"Hey, how about that! Real tennis balls."

The box was nearly filled with them. Yellow and some turning green. Worn and dirt-stained. Still, they didn't look too bad.

Johnson picked up two and flipped them in his hand. "I got to warn you, tennis isn't easy. I'll probably work your tail off."

He could feel his dark mood fading. Going off somewhere. "You pretty good at this game, huh?"

"I played a lot in college."

Owen whistled. "College? You a college man, Johnson? Hey, man, what you doing here with all us fuck-ups?"

"Filling in my time. Like you cats. I'm a premed student. I need the bread I make working summers with you fuck-ups." Johnson shook the box again meaningfully. "You still interested? You want me to teach you the game?"

Owen rubbed his arms. That tennis might be something. He'd seen the guys playing on city park courts. They moved around pretty good and they hit hard. Some of the assholes came charging up and hit too hard and knocked it into the high wire fence. Okay,

41

so you were an asshole, but it didn't seem to hurt none. They looked like they were enjoying it.

He looked down at the rake. The long bent tooth edges were worn and filmed with dirt. Man, it looked used!

"How about that gismo?" he said. "You probably get to working my tail off with that mother, too. Right? I mean, supposing I get to play some tennis with you today, you're gonna make me sweat pushing that tomorrow. Right?"

Johnson looked at him as if surprised. "Tomorrow? Man, this ain't that kind of country club. How about right after the tennis lesson?"

He was able to smile at Johnson. Return his look of mock surprise. "Right after? Like how soon after? You trying to kill me my first day?"

"We call it paying for your pleasure, man. After you learn how to use the racket, you learn how to use the rake. No sweat. Okay?"

Owen groaned. Making the nice feeling last longer. "Oh, man. You are really something. I got the feeling this really ain't no country club after all."

"That is for sure," Johnson said. Then, "You ever see a tennis match, Kirby?"

"Uh-uh. In my neighborhood, we don't dig tennis. We play other games."

"Yeah. I'll bet." Johnson took time to look him over. "You look strong. But you don't need brute power to be a tennis player. You can use the other guy's power and shove it back to him. What you need is speed and good reflexes. You look like you might move fast enough."

"Fast enough?" Owen grinned. "Man, there's nobody faster. That's one thing we don't have to worry about."

"That a fact?" Johnson murmured. He put the box of tennis balls down. He pointed across the field. "See the tree? The tall pine all alone out there? Think you can beat me to it?"

"Hey, man, you're an old college man."

Johnson shrugged. "Any time you're ready. Start us off."

Owen smiled. He took a quick breath. Leaning forward, he said, "Okay. Let's go, man!"

He took off, feeling himself light and free, a powerful machine turned loose. After a few yards, he didn't see Johnson and turned his head. Too late, he saw the blurred form as Johnson rocketed past him.

Johnson was leaning against the pine, tossing a ball casually in the air, catching it neatly as Owen came up.

"Guess I should have told you," Johnson said, "track was my main gig at college. I used to do 9.3 for the hundred."

Jesus, he thought, he breezed right by me like I was standing still!

He couldn't understand it. He had always been faster than anybody on the street. He looked at Johnson's legs, powerful bunchy muscles gleaming black under the faded shorts. The bands of muscle twitched as if alive under Johnson's skin.

43

Man, he's really built! It ain't only his legs either. He's like a fucking rock all over. Lookit those arms!

Johnson read his mind. He clapped his hand on Owen's shoulder. "Don't take it to heart, man. There's a lot of technique in learning how to sprint, too. Just having natural speed isn't enough." Before Owen could answer, Johnson tossed the ball to him.

He snapped it up roughly in the air. It felt light in his hand and he bounced it a few times off the dirt, getting his wind back.

Johnson laughed. "Now you ready to go out on the court with me so I can really run you ragged?"

"Man," he said, gasping, "you are really in shape."

"Got to be," Johnson said. "That's what it's all about if you want to be an athlete."

Owen sucked air and felt his thudding heart slow. He took a deep breath. The morning air was so fragrant he could taste it. He felt good. He couldn't remember feeling that way before. Relaxed and loose. Wanting to smile.

Going goofy, he thought, and scratched his head. Maybe I ain't used to all that fresh air.

Johnson moved and started jogging easily across the field. Owen shook his head. He moved off after Johnson and then pulled up alongside, matching strides. Johnson turned his face and smiled.

"You'll be okay, Kirby. No sweat."

He jogged with Johnson, feeling strange, light-footed. He lifted his shoulders as he ran and swung his arms. He ran with the new buoyant sensation flooding his insides, wondering what was happening.

44

What's this greaseball want?

"Hi, Kirby. I'm Dick Gomez. How we doing?"

Owen grunted, "Okay." He leaned on his rake. He had noticed the slender Mexican-American counselor leading the second group of boys. Gomez was always cheerful. Whistling.

"You're a group leader like Johnson, huh?"

"Only I'm a Chicano. That's the main difference."

"I know, man. Who takes care of the littlest group?"

"That would be Ed Brandon. You met him yet?"

He shook his rake handle meaningfully. "I been too busy. You and him college men like Johnson?"

"You have to be for this kind of social worker job. I'm a law student up at Berkeley. Brandon is premed like Johnson. He's pretty good with the young kids."

Owen knuckled sweat off his forehead. He looked down at the ground. He already could see about twenty feet of dirt he had carefully turned over. He looked at it with pride and affection. *I did that mother all myself, man.*

"Looks good," Gomez said. "You're getting the hang of it."

"I guess. You working up here for the money, too?"

45

Gomez grinned. "It's the onliest reason, man."

"Yeah. Maybe you do it for kicks. Running us so hard."

Gomez looked surprised. "Run you hard? Man, we baby you guys."

"Uh-huh." He turned his hand over. It was blistered and raw. He blew on it. "Any more babying and I'd be in a hospital."

Gomez took his hand. He touched the edges of the blisters with gentle fingers. "You got to be kidding, Kirby. This big one on top isn't from pushing a rake."

"It ain't?"

"Right. You get that kind playing tennis."

He looked at his right hand. "How can you tell?"

"I took four years college, remember?" His strong white teeth flashed. "Also, I saw you playing before with Johnson."

Owen shook his head. "Yeah. College, huh?"

Gomez laughed. "Yeah. But I was an expert on blisters before I went. Look here."

Gomez turned his hands over. Owen felt thick calluses on his palms and fingers. "You got me beat, man. How you get those?"

"Digging ditches."

"No crap?"

Gomez rubbed his hands together briskly. "Johnson and I come from ghetto-barrio areas, just like you, man. We had to fight to get an education. Work our way through college. I handled concrete on construction jobs, dug ditches, laid pipes for sewers, cut trees, carpenter work—anything to make a buck. Johnson did the same. If you decide on college, you'll have to do the same bit."

"Who, me? College?" He snickered. "I ain't been in school since junior high. My first year."

Gomez whistled. "So you blew a few years. You can go back. Make it up if you want to. It could be worth it."

Owen shook his head side to side deliberately slowly. "No way, man. Me and school didn't hit it off right. I was always in some hassle. Getting sent down. Being chewed out. Some I did, some I didn't do. But it don't make no difference. Either way, you get your ass in a sling. No, man—no way. I ain't never going back to that chickenshit."

Gomez picked up the rake. Pushed it back and forth.

"Okay, let's say you don't go back. What's left for you? You get out of here. You go back on the street. Next thing you know, you'll be running with gangs. Maybe killing people."

"Yeah, I guess so."

"Maybe you don't kill somebody. Maybe somebody kills you."

He nodded. "Yeah. It could happen."

Gomez spat in the dirt. His gentle smiling look was gone. His dark eyes were brooding. "I've been through all that, Kirby. It's crazy. I just wish I could get it through your head. You're heading for a dead end, man. Can't you see for yourself that's the way it will go? That it's stupid? Here, take a look at this."

47

Owen hadn't noticed the thin white line running behind Gomez's jawline. It reached from his ear downward at an angle to the center of his throat.

"Somebody bladed me in a gang fight. Sure, I used to run with gangs. I'm an expert there, too. You want to know what I did to the cat who cut me? I split his head open with a Coke bottle." He shrugged, throwing his hands apart. "So we were both lucky. Neither one of us died. You think that's bullshit?"

Owen shook his head. "Yeah, man, okay, I believe you. So shit, what's the difference it's stupid? You know? So okay, I'm stupid, what the fuck, I mean, it don't matter, see? Like it figures, it figures I'm gonna fuck up some way. Now if you move your ass, I can push this motherfucking rake around. Johnson, he don't like it, he don't like it at all if I dog it, come up with some asshole excuses. Okay?"

Gomez stepped aside, and Owen dug the long teeth of the rake fiercely into the ground. It snagged and he pulled hard, cursing it. "It's a lotta work for some fucking grass," he said. "Who needs grass? Or whatever kind of shit they expect to grow here."

Gomez stood off, watching silently as Owen fought the stubby cluttered patch of ground. His voice sounded gentle again. "Maybe you're not as stupid as you think, Kirby. Have you been to see Dr. Samuels yet?"

Owen shook his head, the sweat flying off his face. He kept his back bent, eyes on the ground. He jerked the rake free. Rocks and a torn twisted root were locked in the rake teeth. He glared, bent and tore the root

48

away. He grabbed the stones and hurled them high into the distance.

"Goddamn rocks!" He extended the rake again, smoothing the deep uneven furrow. "No, man. Who's Doc Samuels?"

"Ask Johnson."

Owen pulled the rake close to him. He leaned on it. He stared angrily at Gomez. "How come, man? Don't you know?"

Loud angry voices sounded behind them from the wing area of the cottages. Gomez jerked his head. "Sorry. Somebody needs cooling off. *Adiós, amigo.*"

Owen scowled, watching Gomez lope off. Yeah, he said under his breath, let's see you cool some of them cats off. This country club is too peaceful to believe. There's a lot of mean, tough dudes up here. They ain't forgot so soon how to stomp or cut up some other cat.

After yard duty, he showered off. A note was pinned on the blanket of his bunk. "Report to administration building. See Dr. Samuels." It was signed in a large scrawl. Robert A. Adams, Director.

After evening chow, he showed Johnson the Adams note. "Who's this Doc Samuels, Johnson?"

Johnson thumped the top of his head. "He's our psychiatrist. He's a good man, Kirby. Comes up here often."

Owen sniffed. "A shrink? Who needs him?"

Johnson smiled. "Who don't? Everybody needs help. But it's part of the deal here, man. Samuels will ask

49

you things, give you some aptitude tests. He'll check you out so we'll know more about you, what makes you tick."

Owen scowled. "They already did that, Johnson. Man, they got me down on a million pieces of paper."

"That was another kind of question form for the juvenile court. This is something else. It's another level. Deeper. Don't think you can fool the man, Kirby. He'll know if you start putting him on."

He registered outraged innocence. "Who, me? Putting him on? What for? I don't even know the dude."

Johnson cuffed him roughly across the shoulders. "You let Doc Samuels work that out. It's his specialty. Me, I got enough trouble getting you to hit a ball back to me."

"Them balls are no good, Johnson, they're shit. They are too fucking used up, you know? The mothers fly they're so light. How about we do some baseball instead? I mean, you got a ball up here that's for fucking real. Like with a cover on it, you know?"

Johnson grimaced. "Baseball? We got enough baseball players up here. I need somebody good enough at tennis for me to work out with."

"So what you want with me?"

Johnson shrugged. His dark face was expressionless. "I thought you were coming along pretty good. You've got the makings of a good tennis player."

He looked stricken. "You got to be kidding. Me?"

"That's right. You've got good reflexes, plenty of speed. And above all, you want to win. You've got the

50

real killer instinct, man. That's the most important."
The big counselor spread his hands. "I'm talking about
tennis, dig?"

"That straight?"

"Straight out, man. You can be good. Real good."

He walked away from Johnson pleased. Well, shit,
he said to himself, now how about that?

Dr. Manuel Samuels was pudgy and pale, a middle-
aged balding man with sad brown eyes. He sat at his
desk unsmiling, looking tired.

"Sit down, son. I'll just ask you some questions. You
try to answer them the best way you can. There's no
right or wrong. They're only questions."

Owen nodded, bristling inside. *No right or wrong?*
Man, that is bullshit.

He sat at the angled side of the desk close to Samuels.

"A lot of these questions may strike you as foolish.
This one, for instance. Do you like girls?"

"Huh?"

"Girls. How do you feel about them? Do you like
them?"

He scratched his cheek. "What's that got to do with
anything? I ain't up here because I bladed any girls."
He tried to peer across the desk at the paper under
Samuels' hand. "Maybe you got me mixed up. I'm
Kirby."

Samuels nodded peacefully. "I know. The question
is about girls. Try to answer."

He shook his hands at Samuels. "It was a couple of

dudes who jumped me. I cut some of them. What's girls got to do with it?"

"Not too much," Samuels said, coughing into his hand. "I'd just like you to tell me your reaction to girls. How you feel about them."

Owen slumped back in his seat. "Jeez, I dunno. They're okay, I guess. I don't mess with them much. They're too damn screechy, man. You know?"

Samuels marked something on the paper.

Well, shee-it! What was I supposed to say?

"All right," Samuels said. "How do you feel about your father?"

"My who? My father? Man, he cut out so long ago, I don't even remember him. I couldn't even tell you what he looked like."

"Was he good to you? Could you remember that?"

"No way, man. I'm not putting you on, Doc. When he left, I was only a baby."

"Did he ever beat you? Hurt you?"

"I don't know, man. Honest, it was a long time ago."

"Did he ever buy you things? Toys, for example."

"Maybe. I don't know. I know he didn't buy me no Cadillac."

Samuels smiled. "We're even there. Mine didn't, either." Samuels picked up a half-smoked cigar and struck a match to it. He waved the smoke away. He picked up some papers. "This form states your mother is your sole support. Is that correct?"

Owen shrugged. "Yeah, I guess. When she's working. Otherwise, the welfare people give us the bread."

"What kind of work does she do?"

His ears suddenly felt very hot. He waved the cigar smoke away although he knew that had nothing to do with it. He shook his head. "Beats me, Doc."

Samuels pushed away the papers and looked at him. "You honestly don't know?"

He wagged his head earnestly. "No, sir. I never asked."

She's on the sauce so much, I bet she don't even know herself.

"Well, does she do housework, do you think?"

Say yeah, jerk, he told himself. *What difference does it make?* He raised his hand. "Yeah, Doc. That's it. Housework."

Dr. Samuels took some cards out of a tray on the desk. "Now I'm going to show you these ink-blot pictures. You tell me what you see. All right?"

"Sure. You want to know about that one, huh? That's real easy, man. This dude here is falling down. He's been cut with a blade. You see all that stuff? It's blood."

Samuels took the card back and studied it. "That's very interesting," he said.

7

He couldn't sleep. He stared into the darkness beyond his bunk. Dr. Samuels had said something before they were done.

"The trick is to find one's own becoming of a person." Then looking at him directly, Samuels said, "It's not easy. We all have to work hard at it. Grownups, too. Give it some thought, son."

Words always threw him. What did it mean?

The man McKeon must have found it. He looked like what he was. McKeon and being a probation man were the same. Dr. Samuels had it. Adams, too. Johnson? Well, he couldn't tell about Johnson yet. Johnson was too many things.

Voices raged inside his head. They weren't his.

"Slut!" the man voice said. "Two-bit slut!"

The woman voice was blurry. "Look who's talkin'! Big man! Big windbag! You'd take pennies from a blind man. You ain't been outta the gutter since the day I met you."

There was the sound of something breaking. A dish maybe? The man cursed. Then he hit her. She cursed back and threw another thing. He hit her again. He

54

knocked her down and there was a wide smear across her mouth.

Hey, how do I know that? he wondered.

Because you were there, stupid.

Jeez, I forgot all about it. I must've been little.

He didn't want to look at the small print in the newspaper. It was down near the bottom of the page. He didn't want to look at it but she made him. She held his head and shoved it right under his nose.

"Go on, read it," she said in a fierce tone. "Someday you'll be asking about your father. Maybe I won't remember. So you damn well better read it now!"

His eyes hurt. The printing was very small and blurry. Maybe he was crying.

Yeah, he said, I guess.

J. C. Kirby, small-time hoodlum, was shot and killed last night as the result of an argument in a neighborhood bar. Witnesses said Kirby, once a professional middleweight boxer, provoked the fight by an assault upon another patron at the Mid-Nite Bar.

J. C.? I wonder, did he have a name?

He felt his cheek wet. He rubbed it off with the knuckles of his right hand. Jesus! he told himself, don't tell me you're still crying about that!

Moonlight bathed the small cottage floor. He sat up. He was surprised to hear himself laughing. *I wonder what ol' Doc Samuels would have said if I told him that?*

No, sir. I don't remember my father.

No, sir. He cut out long ago.

55

No, sir. When he left, I was only a baby.

He dangled his feet over the side of his bunk. *Well, anyway,* you *know. It don't matter what you told Samuels.*

Yeah, he said silently, but you want to know something? When he asked me, I swear I didn't know.

Crap.

No kidding. That's the truth.

Aw, go back to sleep, jerk. You said you were little and you read the paper. How could you read the newspaper if you were so goddamn little?

I don't know. I guess she made me.

He didn't remember falling asleep. When he woke up the next morning, his body was curled up into a tight ball. His thumb was in his mouth. He jerked it out angrily.

You better cut that out, he told himself.

He looked around guiltily. Everybody was sleeping. *Jesus, that was close!*

The indoor basketball court and gym building was being made ready for the meeting. A few folding chairs were scattered around the sides. The room began to fill up. Owen came in with his group. Boys were already sitting on the shining floorboards. He noticed they were forming a huge circle, leaving the center open.

He saw Johnson. "What's happening, Johnson? We seeing some kind of show?"

Johnson held a folding card table. "It's a regular weekly happening. A rap session."

"How you mean, man?"

Johnson put the table down on its edge. "It's like your own show. Everybody gets a chance to gripe. Get what's buggin' him off his chest."

"Like what?"

Johnson shrugged. "It's up to you and the guys. Whatever pisses you off. Here's your chance to bitch about it."

"What good will that do?"

"Adams and Dr. Samuels started it. The idea was group therapy. That means everybody helps everybody else."

"How the fuck we do that?"

Johnson shook his head. "You'll see." He pointed to a space. "Just set your ass down there. Watch what's happening."

"How do I help anybody? I don't know half the dudes here."

"You'll know them better after tonight. Now fall down somewhere. I got to set up some things."

Johnson moved away. Owen watched the others. They were horsing around. Laughing. They seemed to know what this thing was about.

If they know, it can't be too bad. They're feeling good so it can't be heavy.

Gomez was talking to the red-headed Brandon. Gomez waved. Owen walked stiff-legged to the fringe. He started to walk over the outstretched legs of those sitting up front.

"Flop anywhere, Kirby," Gomez said. "No reserved places here."

He didn't know anybody. He still hadn't spoken to anybody. Only Johnson and Gomez. He didn't trust the other bastards.

Make up your mind, for Christ's sake! Where the fuck you gonna sit?

A hand touched his elbow. He looked up and saw Adams. "First time for you, Owen? Well, here's a good place. You'll be able to see and hear everything."

Adams leaned down, tapping shoulders. He murmured words softly. The boys moved for him and made room. Then Owen was sitting on the floor inside

58

the third concentric ring. Satisfied, Adams nodded and moved off. He was exchanging easy banter with the boys as he went past.

Owen sat stiffly, frowning. He hugged his arms close to him, keeping himself separate. He knew some of them by name, the older ones from his group.

The blacks, Dye, Brown, tough ex-gang leaders.

The Chicanos, Santos, Garcia.

Hawkins, May. Whities.

They were animated, laughing. Exchanging swift gibes. The hardness dissolved from their faces. He shrugged. He felt distant, apart from that friendly feeling, and from them.

Fuck 'em.

He knew these dudes. They weren't fooling him with that clowning-around bit. They'd stomp out anybody if they felt like it.

They seemed to dig Adams. Maybe because he came on easy, not leaning heavy on anybody. Yeah, Adams was cool.

He thought it was funny that Dr. Samuels had asked him if he liked girls. He forgot to ask him if he liked *anybody.* He sat hard-eyed, wondering if he ever had.

What for?

Funny about Johnson though. Johnson really was something else.

Adams stepped into the center. "For the benefit of you newcomers, I'll explain the gripe session."

Owen hunched forward. He tried to understand what Adams was saying. Somebody laughed. Somebody else whistled. The camp director kept on talking.

He didn't get it. If that was all it was, how come everybody was turned on? It was no big deal. Anybody could step up there. That was the hot seat. You got a few beefs off your chest. Anybody was entitled to ask questions. Anybody could comment.

There weren't any rules. Nobody was in charge.

It was all theirs, Adams said, and walked off. "Who wants to start us off?" he called.

Owen didn't see anybody volunteering. Then there was a scuffle near him. One of the boys was being pushed to his feet. His friends prodded him, hooting. They were middle groupers. The kid stumbled to the center. He was red-faced. His eyes were rolling and nervous. He looked pale under the white overhead beam of lights.

Johnson called from the side. "Just give us your name. Then give us your beef."

The kid nodded. He swallowed hard and swung his hands. "Frank Allen. Sometimes I'm called Frankie."

There were whistles. Applause.

"Come on, Frankie. Let it all hang out."

"Yeah. Drop your pants."

The crowd roared. The boy clenched his fist and made a threatening gesture. His face glistened. "Okay, you bastards, I heard that. Anyway, what I want to talk about is the food. It's crappy food. It stinks. Maybe it's okay for pigs."

A boy at the rear started to clap. He yelled, "Right on!"

Another yelled, "If it's okay for pigs, how come you're always cutting back for seconds, Frankie?"

"Don' you know, man? That's 'cause he's a pig hisself."

The crowd jeered and shouted. A boy near Owen cupped a hand to his mouth. "Oink! Oink!"

Others joined in the snuffling pig sound. They grunted loudly. Some got up and danced around, grunting, raising their arms, bending them high at the elbows, snuffling. "Oink, oink!"

Owen sat unmoved. *That food ain't so bad.*

He wondered if the camp cook was here tonight, a plump affable Chinese called Fatso Lee. Maybe he had to attend the gripe sessions too? Maybe he had to catch it like everybody else. Promise to do better.

Owen screwed his head all around. He didn't see the cook anywhere. When his eyes swung back, the boy in the center hot seat was making shortstop gestures as the crowd chanted in unison: "Oink, oink, oink, oink!"

He yelled back, trying to be heard over the clamor. He grabbed his upper right arm with his left and thrust his right fist up. "Up yours, you mothers!" he seemed to be shouting.

Owen watched. The catcalls grew louder. The crowd laughed and hooted.

I don't dig this, he thought.

Johnson walked up slowly. He raised his arms and moved his hands. The noise subsided. "Come on, guys. Hold it down for a minute. We want to hear what Frankie has to say, don't we?"

61

"We already heard," a boy yelled. "He digs garbage."

"Oink! Oink! Oink!"

"Don't feel bad, Frankie. Next time I give you mine."

Johnson put his hand on the red-faced boy's shoulder. "Anything else you want to say, Frankie?"

Frankie nodded. His throat worked convulsively. He grimaced and took a step forward. "Screw youse all!"

Over the renewed din and hooting, Johnson said, "You all hear that?"

A boy toward the rear raised his hand. "No, man, I was asleep. What he say?"

"He say somethin' awful, man," another said. "He say he wants to screw us all."

They laughed, applauded, stomped their feet on the floor. Owen swiveled his head. The responses were too swift to catch. He looked at their jeering faces. *I don't get it.*

"What he mean, 'screw us all'?" a boy said.

A boy up front tumbled on the floor. His arms were out, pleading. "Me first, Frankie boy. I been here too long."

Those behind him pulled at his feet and he went down. They slid him back. "No, man. You got to wait your turn."

"That's right, man. We all in this together. We don't want Frankie playin' no favorites."

"Hey, do he mean screw us one at a time or all together? Maybe we got to line up."

"He means all together, man. He got all that garbage inside him what's makin' him a big man."

They whistled. "How big, Frankie? Let's see what you got?"

"I don' think he got too much. He used it up last night playin' with it."

"Hey, man, this for free or you willing to pay?"

Then Johnson was asking Frankie if he had anything more to say. The boy shook his head. Johnson patted his back. "Well, you did okay, Frankie. Thanks for stepping up."

The boy walked off to applause and cheers. He found his seat and scuffled to sit down. Johnson raised his hands.

"Before we get the next griper, let's check. Who agrees with what Frankie said about the food? Raise your hands."

Owen sat unmoving. Hands shot up like flags. Johnson appeared to be counting. "Okay. Anybody who likes the food?"

One hand went up. They roared and pushed him down, but laughing. "One out of sixty. That ain't much," Johnson said.

Adams leaned forward to say something. Johnson cupped a hand to his ear. "Mind repeating that, Mr. Adams?"

Owen watched Adams come through the ring. Adams bowed in a clowning way to the applause. "We all gave Frankie Allen a rough time. But apparently he told us what we all secretly thought. Something is wrong with the food here. Do you all agree to that?"

They whistled. Stomped their feet.

Owen's lip curled. *Jerks!*

"Right on, man!"

"You better believe it!"

"Oink! Oink!"

Adams held up his hands. They quieted. "Sounds like we'll have to get better food here or fire the cook."

"Yeah, man. That's groovy!"

"Fire Fatso Lee!"

A kid cupped his hands and shouted, "Kill the cook!"

They began to clap in unison, chanting steadily. "Kill the cook! Kill the cook! Kill the cook!"

Adams wagged his head, smiling. His hands went up again. "Let's keep that in reserve until we give our Mr. Lee another chance. Okay?"

"All right. Give the mother one more time and that's it!"

"Shape him up or ship him out!"

Adams nodded. He raised his right fist clenched. "I'll talk to the mother about it myself first thing tomorrow." He walked off to thundering stomping and hand-clapping.

A boy on Owen's left nudged him sharply with his elbow. The boy's eyes were gleaming. "That Adams— he's really somethin', ain't he?"

Owen nodded. "Yeah." *Who cares?* he thought.

He turned away, folding his arms. He didn't have much to say to these other fuck-ups. *Stay outta my way and I'll do you the same.*

There were new murmurs of excitement. Another boy was stepping into the vacant circle. He was black, tall, one of the older boys. He moved easily with a nonchalant grace.

"I'm Justin Dye," he said.

Somebody in the rear whistled. It was two-tone, a derisive sound. Dye looked out, dark eyes glittering. He stood slender and erect, with hands jammed against his narrow hips. His face was hard, glaring at them all with contempt.

A young boy tittered. "My, don' he look mad!"

Dye grimaced. He pointed his forefinger at the boy. "You better hope I ain't mad when I see you on the street, man. I'm headman of the Nomads in L.A. You dig?"

Owen leaned forward in rapt attention. He had noticed Dye at the cottage next door to his with the older boys. Dye seemed always cool and withdrawn. He did his yard duties quietly. He carried authority with deadly assurance. None of the boys bugged Dye. They seemed afraid of him.

No wonder, Owen thought. Headman for the Nomads —man, you got to be tough.

The Nomads. They were one of the biggest street gangs. Even the Sinners stayed clear of them. The Sinners were a larger gang with older members. But they never crossed into Nomad turf.

Owen thought he could understand now. There was something about Justin Dye that shook you up. He sort of spooked you. He looked like one mean, hard cat. Headmen of other gangs wouldn't want any part of a hassle with Justin Dye.

Yeah, he said to himself, but he's up here, too. They got him sent up just like you and the other cats. Headman or no, they put him out of business.

Dye's naked hostility sobered the hecklers. They sat still while he spoke. His voice was furry, oddly warm and musical. When it went flat was when he was dangerous, and the audience recognized him for what he was and gave him respect.

He don't hide nothing. He lets it all hang out like he feels.

"I'm not bitching about the food," Dye said. "What I'm talking about is the bull they feed us. Telling us how free we is to choose. Man, that's a crock. What we got to choose?

"Okay, so I took a fall like the rest of you. In a year, maybe two, we all gonna be back on the street. What we gonna do? How we gonna make out? Do we get to choose? Bullshit!"

Somebody began clapping his hands. Dye turned his head and looked annoyed. "Cut that crap, man. Save it for when I'm done."

Owen watched the hand-clapper flinch, drop his hands as if they had been burned. *Yeah, this Dye's got the power, all right. He can zing you, just like that.*

"Say we go back doin' like we used to doin' on the street," Dye said. "A little rip-off here and there. Cut some cat who steps out of line. Get a little property. Maybe some operation going. Dig? And what happens? The Man comes down on us again saying what we doin' is wrong.

66

"What they doin', all them fat cats, not payin' no income tax, rippin' off whatever they can get, selling things that fall apart and don't stand up, raising prices —*shee-it!* Now ain't that a bigger rip-off? All them gas and oil cats, man, they stiffing us blind! We the ones who got to pay, and them mothers sticking it to us every day, driving us right up the wall, and shit, nobody says nothin'—they got it made and nobody says nothing about how they screwing us.

"But us cats, all we got to do is step out of line only one time. You cut some dude and whammo—there is the Man to flag you down, put you away. Two years, the Man says. Lock up the mother, he too dangerous to let be. Don' let him loose, he might hurt somebody. If *we* want a war, only *we* say who can do the killing, dig? Only *we* is entitled, see? Only that *we* ain't got nothing to do with us. The kind of *we* that *we* is, that's the kind them mothers got to put away."

Owen was nodding tensely. *That's the truth. That's the way it is.*

A boy behind Owen yelled, "How many in your gang, man?"

Dye shrugged. "Fifty—sixty."

"How many dudes you cut up yourself?"

Dye's eyes glittered. "Maybe a few."

The crowd laughed. Dye smiled and they hooted and began to whistle. The barriers were down, Owen noticed, only at Justin Dye's indulgence.

A boy said, "You only cut a few? Man, that's nothin'. Maybe you ain't so tough."

67

"My kid sister already done that many. And she not even in junior high yet."

Dye laughed. "Your sister sounds okay, man. Maybe we let her run with the brothers when she grows up."

"How come you get two years for only cuttin' up some dude?" an older boy said. "Around my way, you allowed that for a starter."

Dye rubbed his jaw. "Dunno, man. Where you from?"

Another interrupted. "Maybe Dye, he only countin' the cut-ups, not the shot-ups."

"Yeah, man," another called. "How many cats has you really wasted?"

Dye hesitated, then shook his head, smiling.

A boy yelled, "He can't count that high. Justin ain't never had that new math."

"New math—*shee-it!* Don' mention that mother!"

"Hey, Justin," a boy said. "How you fixed for grass? You bring some up with you?"

"Yeah, Justin," another said, "you pass us some pot, we make up your bed for you every day."

There were whoops. Dye stood smiling. His saturnine lean face glowed. He shook his head. "I don't dig grass, baby." He tapped the center of his forehead. "That stuff scrambles your head. I leave that alone."

There were cries of dismay. "You don' need no head up heah, man. Heah they just works your ass off."

Dye shrugged negligently. "That's what you get for runnin' against the Man. Next time you'll have to play it smart. Play it cool."

68

A boy whistled. "Cool is crap. You is cool, man, an' you up here same as all us mothers."

Dye laughed. "That's for sure. Guess I ain't cool."

"Who taking care of your Nomads now, Justin? Who the new headman?"

Dye fixed the last speaker with a cold, arrogant look. "Ain't nobody took my place. When I get outta here, I am still headman."

A boy waved his hand to attract Dye's attention. "You can't do that, man. When you get outta here, you has got to give up runnin' with gangs. Your probation man gonna straighten you out on that. You run, you right back heah."

"That's right," another called. "That's what they do. They waiting for you to run one more time. Maybe they send you to a worster place than here."

Dye shook his head. "Well, that's what I was saying. You got to have gangs. You got to run. We got to get these p.o. people to understand. The way the street is, you got to have gangs. You by yourself, man, you got no chance. On the streets, it's the gangs what do the talking. About time these people knew that. How else you going to go about your business without being cut or stomped out? What they expect us to do, just smile when some dudes stop us? Show them the other cheek?"

They began to whoop. They laughed and waved their arms.

"Come on, Justin, baby. Lean over. Show us your cheeks, man."

"Yeah, brother. Maybe it got a stamp on it what says Headman!"

Owen tensed, biting his lower lip. He couldn't believe they would ride Dye this way, not take him seriously. He turned his head. They were all hooting and laughing at Dye.

Dye smiled. He held his arms straight out and bowed his head in a quick bobbing gesture. They quieted down. Dye said, "Okay, brothers. Let's leave it before it becomes too heavy. That's all I got to say for this meeting."

The cheers were mingled with boos as he walked off.

Dye moved with languid grace in a direct line. He stepped over bodies in his way. When blocked, he snapped his fingers sharply. They responded and moved to give him room. Some patted his pants legs as he passed through.

"Right on, Justin."

"You tol' 'em where it's at, baby."

"Gangs is boss, man. You damn right."

They were anxious to please. Smiling up to him.

Yeah, the game is over now, Owen thought. They won't say boo to his face. They know he's the Nomad headman.

Hey, maybe he can help me when I get back to L.A. He could put me straight to a lotta things.

His inner voice mocked. Yeah, he don't even know you. You ain't spoken a word to him so far. He don't know you from shit.

Well, there's plenty of time. Maybe some day we'll

70

talk. Only I tell you one thing, I ain't sucking up to him like them cats.

His eyes burned watching Dye until the gang leader sat. Owen looked around, wondering who would be next.

Long as it ain't me, he said silently. I got nothing to say to these mothers.

"Mail call!" Johnson shouted.

He came out of the bunkhouse blinking in the morning glare. Johnson was calling names, passing out letters. He walked on by.

Who's gonna write me? I don't know nobody.

He took a white card out of his pocket. It listed his activities for the day. Yard duty. Repair shop. Field duty. Classes in the evening.

Owen scowled at the card. He thought he was through with school, but up here they told him he wasn't. Not until he was sixteen, according to California law.

He folded the card and pushed it deep into his pocket. Well, it ain't no big deal, he told himself. It ain't like you got to pass. All you got to do is be there.

He was getting used to the place. It was becoming a good feeling to look out into the distance. You looked maybe twenty miles to the nearest mountain and you didn't have to see one crummy building. Funny, he thought, you never see a crummy-looking tree.

After the gripe session, he lay in his bunk. Others visiting in the room clustered about Joey Hawkins, another L.A. gang leader. Hawkins was big for his age, a hefty six-footer weighing close to 200 pounds. His voice was high and nasal.

A boy said, "You're a headman too, ain't you, Joey?"

Hawkins sat reclining on his cot, arms folded behind his thick blond hair. He snickered. "Well, I ain't no Justin Dye. But, yeah, I run the Tips."

The Tips? I never heard of the Tips.

Then he remembered there were over three hundred street gangs in L.A. and nobody would know them all. He squinted through half-closed eyes at Joey Hawkins. He didn't convey the same deadly cold menace of Justin Dye. But he was big and he looked powerful. That could be enough to run a gang.

It didn't do him no good though. He's up here too, same as Justin Dye. Same as me. Same as these other assholes.

"What you up for, Joey?"

"Two years. Maybe less, the Man said."

"What they get you for?"

Hawkins laughed. A snuffling sound. "Man, I got so many counts, you wouldn't believe it."

"Oh, yeah? Like what?"

He brought his hands away and ticked off the count on his fingers. "Assault, pistol-whipping, robbery, drug abuse and rape."

They whistled. "Rape?"

Hawkins snickered. "It wasn't the first time."

"Yeah, who was it—your sister?"

Their heads turned. A young Chicano had just come in. He stood there grinning. Owen sat up.

Man, that cat is very brave or real crazy.

He felt the sudden tension in the room. Okay, here it is. Here's the time bomb ready to go off.

Hawkins blinked. His deep chest rose but he stayed cool. He made the snuffling laughing sound. Then he flicked his middle finger at the latecomer as if blowing him away. "No, I don't think it was my sister. Maybe she was your sister. Huh? Huh? How about that?"

The Mexican boy shook his dark head, smiling. "Lucky for you I don't have no sister."

The big boy shrugged and scratched his head. "Well, then okay, man. You got no beef, right?"

"That's right." He flipped his hand and walked, whistling, to his bunk at the far end of the room.

Hawkins stared. He pursed his lips and made a thumbing motion. "Who's that little smart ass?"

"Bobby Carmona. He's a 'bean.' You know?"

"Yeah, I know," Hawkins said. He rolled his eyes. "If he don't watch it, he can be a *has*-bean." He snickered again. "You dig? A *has*-been!"

The group around Hawkins laughed.

A boy sat down on the end of Hawkins's bed. "Hey, Joey, this cat Justin Dye. You and your Tips ever tangle with him back in L.A.?"

"No, man. They're central L.A. We're more east. Nowhere near the Nomads. Besides, they got a real big gang. We're kinda small. Maybe twenty or so. That ain't too much, but we do okay. We get a little action."

"You think Dye's tough?"

Hawkins grimaced. "Man, I don't think. I know."

"Yeah? He don't say much."

"That's 'cause he don't have to. You want to stay healthy, just don't mess with that cat. I'm telling you straight. I know guys went over to challenge him. They never come back."

Yeah, Owen thought, leaning back again, I believe it. He decided he didn't like Hawkins. A big asshole. He had to laugh like he had something stuck in his mouth after everything he said. Just a big jerk.

He ain't in the same league with Dye. Dye's got class.

The next morning he came out of the shower after the young Chicano Carmona. A boy pointed to Carmona's legs and whistled through his teeth. "Hey, man, you been in a fire?"

Carmona shook his head. Water sprayed from his glossy long jet hair. "No, *pendejo*. Don' you know nothing? What's on my legs is from the *chocote*—the flogging strap."

"What's that?"

"It's a whip they use. A lead-weighted leather strap. This was in some detention place in Florida. I was running away."

Owen winced at the ravaged skin. He spoke involuntarily. "They whip you?"

The Chicano shrugged. "They put you in the punishment room—the *calabozo*. They throw you on a little bench. Then some big fucking guard stands over you with that mother flogger strap. Man, he beats you till you can't move."

The other boy said, "Why they do that?"

75

"I tole ya. I wasn't able to move, see? So I wasn't able to run away from there. That was the idea."

Owen frowned. He wondered how he would take that.

Carmona laughed lightly. "But I fool them *asquerosos*. I run away soon after for the last time and they never catch me. *Fajarse muy bien los calzones!* You show them you got balls!"

Carmona walked off whistling. The other boy stared after him. He looked at Owen and flicked his hand. "Man, ain't that somethin'?"

Owen nodded. He yawned, stretched. "Yeah. What do you expect from pigs?"

"You ain't shittin', man."

He saw Carmona later. They were doing yard duty together. Owen lifted his hand in a tentative gesture. "Hi."

Carmona grunted acknowledgment. He thrust his shovel into the hard earth. "What for you doin' time, man?"

"I cut up a few dudes what jumped me. I was outta my turf."

Carmona looked him over appraisingly. He turned his head to check the others working the patch of ground.

"Bloods?"

He grimaced. "My own people."

Carmona grunted, turning over the earth. "How many was there?"

76

"Three. They nearly stomped me out."

Carmona spit. "You shoulda killed the bastards when you had the chance." His soft Spanish accent was sharper.

"If I did, where'd I be now, man?"

The wiry Mexican boy grinned. "You got a point, *amigo*. Maybe I better remember that."

"I nearly did it anyway."

"So you was as lucky as them."

"I guess. My name's Kirby, Carmona. What you up for?"

Carmona looked surprised. "Who, me? I didn't do nothin', man."

"Shit you didn't."

Carmona laughed, showing his teeth. "It was a few things. Stealin'. Breakin' and enterin'. Drunk. Resistin' arrest. Breakin' parole. Fightin' with dangerous weapon."

"Man, you been busy."

Carmona heaved another heavy load and leaned on his shovel. "I'm gonna be a lot more busy when I get out."

"You will?" Owen said.

"Why not?" Carmona said. "What else? I ain't running to be president. You got to live. You need the bread. How you gonna get it?"

"Yeah. You're right."

Carmona stood straight. He looked out toward the distant mountains. "We used to own this. All this fuckin'

state of California up and down. Now we got nothin'
and we treated like shit. Man, you can't complain.
You got the right skin."

"Well, shit. I didn't ask for it!"

Carmona smiled. "If you did, maybe you wouldn't
get it."

The color line was always coming up. Even when
he wasn't thinking about it. So now where was he?
The only two he liked were Johnson and Carmona.
One was black, the other brown.

Shee-it! I even like Justin Dye. Man, what is wrong
with you?

Gomez came over. He was wearing shorts. Owen
noticed he had legs like a sprinter. He wasn't big as
Johnson but he moved easily like a trained athlete.

I'd like to see him run against Johnson. He looks fast.

Gomez whistled. "You guys are really working."

"Yeah," Owen said. "Sometimes."

Gomez smiled. "Hey, Carmona, after you finish digging that drainage ditch, you got any other detail?"

"No. After this, I fuck off."

"You want to play some ball?"

"No."

Gomez had the same Spanish pattern in his speech.
They could have been brothers. "I thought you liked
to play ball."

"It's okay."

"Maybe with a lot of practice, some day you could
make a pretty good shortstop for the major leagues."

"Yeah. They're waitin' for me."

Gomez stood close now. He spoke softly. "All right. So baseball is out. Is there something you would like to do?"

Carmona stood up his shovel. He faced the older boy. "I'd like to find a nice fat girl. Can you arrange that?"

Gomez smiled. "Listen, I'd like that myself. Tell me something reasonable. I'm a youth counselor, not a magician."

Carmona wiped sweat from his gleaming face. "Get off my back, Gomez. What you want, man?"

Gomez reached out and jerked the shovel out of the ground. Carmona watched him. Gomez turned and rammed the blade hard. The metal bit into the earth with a crunching sound. He put his foot on the top edge of the blade sending it deeper. He bent and lifted. He dumped the shovel full of dirt over to the side.

"Does that remind you of anything?" Gomez said.

Carmona looked blank. He shook his head.

I don't get it neither.

"I dug a hole in the ground," Gomez said. "When you get out, you'll be doing the same thing. Only you'll be burying yourself in it."

"So what?" Carmona said. "I won't be hurtin' you."

Gomez tightened his jaw muscles. "It's a waste. You need to find direction. Soon you will be at the crossroads. You have to make up your mind whether to go left or right. *Vaya a la izquierda. Vaya a la derecha.*"

"Sorry but I know already. I go the only way I know. Straight ahead. *Siga derecho.*" Carmona shrugged.

79

"Don' worry about me, Gomez. It don't make no difference."

Gomez nodded. He handed the shovel to Carmona. "It won't hurt to think some more about it." He turned to Owen. "Sorry to bust up your conversation. I had to get that off my chest. Maybe you two can help each other. I think you have the same problem. You both give up too easily."

Gomez waved and moved away. A group of boys were lifting a framed siding for a bungalow across the field. Gomez broke into an easy loping run.

Carmona stood watching. Owen said, "What's that all about, man?"

Carmona jerked his head. He spit into his hands. He rubbed them together and took the shovel back. "Gomez knows I run with a tough gang back home. He's tryin' to get me to quit. He ain't a bad guy."

"What you call yourselves?"

"Piratas. That means pirates. We war with the Bloods mostly. It's somethin' to do."

The Piratas! Jeez, they're as tough as the Nomads! No wonder Carmona stood up to Hawkins like he did. Man!

"How about yourself?" Carmona said. "Who you runnin' with?"

"I ain't," Owen said. He waited for Carmona's reaction but there wasn't any. "Maybe when I get out."

"It ain't always no picnic," Carmona said. "You do it if you want to be *muy gallo*."

"What's that?"

80

The Chicano pointed across the ditch. Justin Dye was working in the field. "Like him," Carmona said. "A tough guy. That's *muy gallo*. Somebody who lets you know how good, how tough he is."

Owen noticed Dye wasn't dogging it. He was swinging a pickax with a steady rhythm that showed no sign of slackening. His thin-muscled lean frame was deceptively strong.

"Yeah," he said, turning back to Carmona. "He's for real, all right. How about yourself? You a *muy gallo* too?"

Carmona laughed. "No, but I'm workin' on it."

10   The fight happened suddenly. He passed Hawkins lying on his bunk when he came in from yard duty. The burly leader of the Tips gang seemed asleep. Owen walked down the narrow aisle to the next-to-the-last bunk on the opposite side. The cottage had nine occupants and ten beds. The one opposite him was expected to be filled soon. The last one near the wall was Carmona's, although he was out now like everybody else but himself and Hawkins. There was nearly fifteen minutes before the next work detail. It looked like Hawkins had the right idea sacking out, and he lay down too.

The front door opened. His eyes flicked open as two boys came in. One was Slade who had the first bunk up front next to Hawkins. With him was another white boy he didn't know, from another group cell. There wasn't any rule against visiting. His eyes closed. He heard the murmur of their voices. Hawkins sounded his snuffling laugh.

The front door opened again. He heard a quick shuffling of feet. He saw Hawkins standing now in the center. Carmona came in. The door closed behind him.

Hawkins widened his stance as Carmona walked up. He was blocking the Chicano's path. "Walk around, greaser," he said.

Jesus, here it comes! Owen thought, and sat up.

Carmona laughed. He stepped to one side and Hawkins moved and blocked him there. Carmona stopped. He saw the angular Slade and the other white boy between him and the door. He whistled.

Carmona turned back to Hawkins. "*Muy macho,*" he said softly. "Did I hear you say greaser to me?"

"That's what I said, greaseball."

Carmona sighed. "Okay, man. I wanted to be sure."

He stepped in quickly and kicked Hawkins in the crotch. Hawkins screamed and caught at himself. Carmona threw two fast punches and smashed Hawkins's nose. Hawkins gasped as blood spurted. Carmona hit him with a left to the throat, a right to the heart, a left and right to the pit of the stomach. Hawkins sagged slowly to his knees.

Carmona stood over him. "*Vamos!* Come on, get up, you bastard. I want to kill you."

A birdlike sound came from Hawkins as he tried to breathe. He swayed on his knees. Blood dripped slowly from his face. Carmona turned to the boys behind him at the wall.

"You want some of the action, *hombres?*"

They froze. Their eyes rolled to Hawkins.

Hawkins tilted forward and rested on his hands and knees. He was spitting blood. He slapped the floor with his hand. "Fucking greaser!" he said.

83

Carmona kicked him in the teeth. Bone shattered and Hawkins fell over. He retched and spit out some teeth.

Carmona taunted. *"Primo!* Get up, you big boob! *Vato loco!"*

Hawkins heaved himself back on his haunches. His eyes were glazed. He made a choking sound and spit blood at Carmona's feet. Carmona stepped back and Slade and the other boy grabbed him from behind.

"Get up, Joey. We got him," Slade said.

They had Carmona's arms pinned behind him. He couldn't pull free, and Hawkins got to his feet. He shuffled over to Carmona and looked down at him. He made the snuffling sound and punched Carmona in the belly. Carmona grunted and spit in his face. Hawkins wiped it away with the back of his hand. Then he backhanded Carmona across the face and hit him with his open hand coming back.

Redness blotched Carmona's brown face. His black eyes glittered. "That's the hardest you can hit, *gato?*"

"That's just for openers," said Hawkins.

He spread his legs and hit Carmona with slow ponderous punches. They thudded into Carmona's body and rocked his head back. Carmona grunted with each blow.

Owen felt sick watching. It ain't my fight, he said to himself. Then Hawkins hit Carmona two more times and he hated himself for watching. He got off his bed and ran at Hawkins. He jumped on Hawkins's back before he could throw the next punch. Hawkins stag-

84

gered and fell heavily. They went down together and he rolled aside.

Hawkins looked at him surprised. "You shitass!" he roared. "Whose side you on?"

Hawkins struggled up. He reached for Owen.

Owen backed off. "Three on one," he said. "It ain't fair." He glanced at Carmona and saw him standing there dully. His face was busted up. He looked ready to fall.

"*Por mientras.* Stay out of it, *compañero*," Carmona said through mashed lips. "It's my fight."

Hawkins lunged and jerked Owen toward him. His face was sweating and stained crimson. Owen struck savagely. Fresh blood spattered off. Hawkins gaped and hit him. The blow was high on the chest and drove him back. He caromed into the wall and knew for certain he was going to get whipped. Hawkins was too big and strong.

Hawkins reached out and had one hand around his neck, the other ready to club him when the door opened.

Gomez stepped inside. Hawkins held his blow. Gomez said, "What the hell—" He took a step toward the two boys holding Carmona. "Let him go." Their eyes rolled to Hawkins. Gomez screamed, "I said, let him go!"

They stepped back. Carmona's arms dangled at his sides. "You came just in time," he said to Gomez. "I was killing him." His knees buckled and Gomez caught him.

85

Gomez jerked his chin at Hawkins. "Take your hand off Kirby. I'm putting you all on report for fighting. That's as good a way as any to blow your parole chances."

Hawkins dropped his hand and Owen stepped away. "Come on," Gomez said. "Help me take him to the infirmary."

Carmona brushed away their hands. "I can walk." Outside his legs buckled again. He hugged himself while they walked him. "Man, I'm all busted inside."

"You're not too smart, *camarada*," Gomez said. "You take on a big guy like Hawkins, you're giving away over fifty pounds. Man, that's too much."

Carmona spit blood. His grin was lopsided. "He only hits hard. He can't fight."

Gomez looked at him when they came to the clinic door. "You okay, Kirby?"

"Yeah. I only came in at the end."

"What happened, for Pete's sake?"

He looked at Carmona. Carmona winked. The eye was bloodshot with an egg-shaped bruise under it.

"I guess Hawkins felt he had to prove something."

"Stay away from him. He can be trouble."

"Yeah. I know."

That's no big news. You knew that before, he told himself.

He went back to work on his drainage-ditch detail. He saw Hawkins raking the ground. Hawkins worked his way closer. He had washed the blood off his face but it was stained red. His face was lumpy with welts.

86

His right eye was half-closed. His lip was cut. His nose was bruised and swollen.

Hawkins swept his rake upward. Clods of dirt and stones stung him. "Oh, sorry about that," Hawkins said. "I didn't see you down there."

Owen dug his shovel in deep. He swung the load around and released it. Hawkins didn't expect it. He brushed off some moist clay.

"Okay, shitass," Hawkins said. "If that's how you want it."

It had to happen, he told himself. He only wondered why it took so long.

Johnson came over. Hawkins moved away, raking the ground. Johnson watched him. He stepped to the edge of the ditch.

"I just heard from Dick Gomez. Carmona's got a cracked rib and possible internal injuries." He leaned closer. "Did he lay all that on Hawkins?"

Hawkins was out of earshot. "Man, you should of seen it. He was really beating the crap out of him. Then he got careless. And Hawkins got a little help."

Johnson was looking him over. Owen kept working. "You better watch yourself," Johnson said. "That Hawkins is mean."

"Yeah, but he ain't as good as he thinks. If he fucks with me, I'll kill him."

Johnson whistled. "Oh, come on, man. Be serious."

Yeah, he thought. Maybe it'll be the other way. He'll kill me.

He wondered what Johnson would say if he told him

his old man was killed in a barroom fight. Then he might have to tell Johnson his old man had once been a professional fighter. Johnson might look surprised and say, "What weight did he fight at?" and he would say middleweight. He really didn't know, but that's what the paper said. Then Johnson would ask if his old man was any good. He didn't know that, either. He didn't think so, offhand.

He probably was a bum, he thought, looking down at his hands.

11

He missed Carmona. There was a lot he wanted to talk to the little Chicano about. Manero and Cortese were the other Mexican-Americans in his bunkhouse. They were dull and stolid, without Carmona's light spirit. The blacks were Reed, Bench and Foster. They weren't at all like Johnson. They moved slowly, looked sullen. He couldn't blame them, but he thought, what the fuck, we're all up the creek. There wasn't anybody there, he knew, who would lift a finger when Hawkins started belting him around.

He fretted waiting for Carmona to heal and get out of there. When he thought about it, he was surprised. There hadn't been anybody before that he thought of as a friend.

But that's you, he told himself. Carmona, he might feel different.

The swarthy Manero had the bunk on Owen's left. That night he noticed Carmona's empty bed. He snapped his fingers to get Owen's attention. "Hey, man. Wha' happened to Carmona?"

He shrugged. He didn't want to get into that.

Hawkins spoke loudly from his bed at the front end.

89

"He had an accident." He made the snuffling sound. Manero scowled. *"Cómo?"*

"He's in the hospital," Owen said.

Manero whistled softly. Two beds over, the other Chicano, Cortese, nodded. *"Qué pasa?"*

Manero spoke swiftly in Spanish. Cortese got up. *"Espéreme,"* he said and walked out the front door.

Manero lay back on his bed humming to himself. Owen felt the Chicano's eyes on him.

No way, he thought. *I can't say I'm his buddy. I'm in trouble with Hawkins already. If I blab about him and Slade, he'll really come down heavy on me. Maybe Gomez will fill them in. I gotta keep my nose clean.*

The lights were out when Cortese returned. He walked directly to Manero's bed. They whispered in Spanish. Owen heard names he recognized. Gomez. Carmona. Hawkins. Slade. Kirby.

"El otro?" Manero said.

"Quinn. *En casa a la derecha."*

He found out Quinn is the other joker who helped Slade. The jerk must have shot his mouth off.

He could pick out only a word or two. Finally he gave up listening. They were still whispering when he fell asleep. He thought he heard a scuffling noise in the middle of the night. Manero wasn't in his bunk.

They found Hawkins the next morning in the outdoor shower stall. He was unconscious. He was badly beaten. His body had been stabbed thirty times with a sharp instrument. He was rushed to the hospital in the nearest town.

Stabbed? Owen thought. *What with?*

Johnson showed him later. They filed their plastic toothbrush handles down to a sharp point on the concrete walls. It was as good as a knife.

"It didn't have to be that," Johnson said. "Sometimes they borrow a fork from the mess hall and forget to return it. You can file down a fork to a pretty nasty weapon, too."

Nobody told him any more about it. He saw Santos and Garcia, the two big Chicano ex-gang leaders. He could imagine Manero and Cortese getting their help for the job on Hawkins. He remembered now how the Chicanos always stuck together. While they hated the blacks and fought with them, they hated the whities more.

That Hawkins, he thought. *He thought he was King Shit when he nearly killed Carmona. Jesus, he should'a known they'd get even and rip him off. What an asshole!*

He had to wonder now about Slade and Quinn. *Jesus, they got to be wettin' their pants waiting.*

He remembered how he had dismissed Manero and Cortese as dull compared to Carmona. What they had done showed him he didn't know too much. They did what they had to.

He felt relieved. The passions and hostilities were beginning to hang out. This was the way it had to be with these cats. Nothing was going to change them. The nagging Hawkins was another problem resolved, too. With him out of action, there wasn't much to worry over. If he pulled through and lived, they would probably send him to another juvenile camp. Carmona would get better soon. Maybe they could play tennis together.

Johnson was patient with him. He drilled him over and again with the same shots. *Come in on your serve. Step into your volleys. Watch the ball. Step into it. Hit. Hit the mother. Smash it. Okay. Now we work the backhand. Move. Turn your shoulder. Hit up. Step into it. Hit the mother. Okay. Now we do it all again. Watch the ball. . .*

He was beginning to like the game It was something he looked forward to each day. He didn't remember that happening before.

He liked using the rake. Watching the vegetable garden shape up. Things growing. Those fucking seeds, they all seemed to know what to do once you put them in the ground.

How come I'm still nowhere and that mother seed knows where it's at?

It beat the old life of doing nothing. Doing nothing was a drag. You did nothing over and over and your head died.

The goddamn mother seeds had the secret. You put out and you grow. *Jesus! Man, what's happening?*

He liked the fresh-air feeling in his lungs. It seemed to pep him up. Back home, his ass was always dragging, like everybody else. The only ones who showed any life were on speed. Now he could walk and run all day, work in the fields, really bust his balls, and it wasn't any big deal. A little beat, but a good tired feeling.

92

You ate and slept it off and recharged your batteries, and next morning you were alive again.

He knew he would miss the great distances he could see without his eyes hurting when he got back to the soupy gook of the downtown Los Angeles skies. The mountains on the distant horizon were so sharply etched, he could see every detail. A bird on the wing showed every feather clearly. There wasn't all that crap in between, that invisible blanket in the air.

Still, he cautioned himself. It's like a holiday now, he said silently. You don't got to scratch for food and bread. It's all here waiting for you to reach out and take. Back home, it will be the same story. How you gonna make out when nobody gives you the handout?

Maybe if he worked at something, he could cut it. Only what? If he left the old lady, he'd have to look out for himself all the way. That meant three squares and a room. How was he going to swing that?

He had been on his own nearly all his life hustling anyway. But the old lady offered him the roof over his head. It wasn't much but it beat sleeping in alleys.

He liked to box. Maybe he could turn into a fighter. A lot of the kids in the ghetto and barrio areas became club fighters when they weren't much older than he was. They pulled down a deuce or a fin for a couple rounds. Later when they got older, they made more. Some made it their living.

He thought about that.

Too bad I never knew the old man. He could'a given me some tips, maybe. He was a pro, wasn't he?

J. C. Kirby. *I wonder who he ever beat?*

That Carmona, he thought admiringly. He could be one hell of a fighter. I didn't know you could throw punches so fast. He hit hard, too. Look how he busted up that fucking asshole Hawkins.

Carmona had to be a valuable man with the Piratas gang. He was reckless, unafraid. *Man, who would ever think of starting up with a big goon like Hawkins? You got to be a little crazy in your mind to even think of it.*

He grinned, remembering how Carmona had got off to a good start by kicking Hawkins in the balls. *Yeah, it helps when you know how to fight dirty, too.*

And there he was, like another asshole, telling Hawkins and Slade and that other jerk Quinn that three-on-one wasn't fair. *Jesus, what a jerk! Who fought fair?*

He wondered really how many Chicanos had yanked Hawkins out of his bunk and taken him outside to beat the crap out of him. *It could'a been the whole camp. All they got. Man, I'm glad I didn't tell them nothing about fair!*

He'd have to ask around about the Tips when he got back. Any gang with such an asshole for a leader couldn't be worth a shit.

The Nomads and the Pharaohs were the large gangs in his own neighborhood. Both black. Even if Dye remembered him, he couldn't see running with a black gang. Jesus, his own guys would kill him.

The Huns and the Mumms were the nearest big white gangs. They had a lot of older members. Some of the guys were even married!

94

Jesus, he thought, how can you be married and still want to run with a gang?

He saw Gomez approaching. There was no way he could get Gomez to understand how important it was around his way to be with a gang. Gomez hated gangs.

Gomez looked mean and angry. That wasn't like him.

"Hey, Gomez," he said. "*Qué pasa?*"

Gomez stopped. "You really want to know?"

"Well, sure, man. What's happening?"

"I'll tell you what's happening. Carmona took a powder."

"What?"

"Yeah. He decided not to stick around for the doctors to tell him when he would get better. So he left."

"The hospital?"

"No, *amigo*," Gomez said. "He's gone. He blew the whole camp! I've been looking all over for him. He skipped."

"Man, you sure?"

"Sure I'm sure. Man, now we really got trouble."

"How do you mean?"

Gomez looked at him. "Well, first there was this fight between Carmona and Hawkins, right? Then after Hawkins busts Carmona up, Manero and Cortese and the other Chicanos they got to get even. So you know what happened to Hawkins, right? I understand he'll live, but that's not their fault. They tried hard enough to kill him. And now Carmona's split. How do you think this makes Adams and us look? If you can't guess, I'll tell you. Like a bunch of assholes!"

"Well, shit, man, it ain't your fault."

"No, huh? Go tell it to them."

"Them?" He looked puzzled until Gomez jabbed the air past his shoulder several times. He saw a group of visitors, well-dressed men, walking with the camp director Adams. "Who are them fuckers?"

"Some VIPs from the state board and the capitol. They decided to pay us a visit and see how we're doing."

"How come?"

"A kid busted out of here a couple of weeks ago. Before you got here. He was just picked up in town as a suspect."

"About what?"

"They think he killed somebody. Some old lady."

"And now they're gonna find out about Hawkins and Carmona?"

Gomez patted him. "Man, you got the picture. *Adiós.*"

He looked back at the men with Adams. They had stopped walking now and were standing around. Adams was talking. He was waving his arms. Pointing to this and that.

He felt suddenly sick and very tired inside. *When he gets through pointing, they'll probably ask him where are the walls!*

12 The visitors left. More came the next day. They toured the camp area with Adams. They watched the guys work. They looked in the bunkhouses. They checked the mess hall. Adams didn't look worried. He wore his smile a little tighter but it stayed on.

He heard the scuttlebutt. They were going to put up walls all around. They were going to bring in guards. The whole place was due for a shake-up. Adams might go.

Johnson laughed. "Man, that is crap. A lot of big people were behind this idea of a camp for kids in trouble. They're not going to let what one kid does blow the whole idea. Not a couple of fights, either."

"So what's it all about?" he said.

"It's political. These guys want to show the voters back in their districts that they're on the ball. They've got a little muscle so they try to use it. Relax, nothing will happen. Take my word for it. I've been through this before."

He noticed Justin Dye wasn't worried. Dye surveyed the visitors briefly and turned away. He seemed to regard them with contempt. His manner indicated they weren't much. They were lawmakers. A bunch of fuck-ups who made things harder than they had to be.

Dye's followers at camp hung on every word and gesture of the headman. He already had a small gang without asking for it.

They're all suckin'. They know when they come out, he's the man can do them the most good.

Another with followers was May, headman for a gang known as Blues. They were a white gang from Hollywood known to have a unit of girls calling them-selves Bluebells. May and Hawkins were the only two white ex-gang leaders at camp. With Hawkins out of it, he considered May.

May was one of the older boys, seventeen or older. He was short and stocky, blue-eyed, good teeth. His face looked as if it had been busted one time. He didn't smile much, and like Dye, when he wanted something he snapped his fingers. There was always somebody hurrying over.

When the visitors toured the grounds, May delib-erately stopped working to slouch and stare at them. His unit did the same.

Johnson came over. He spoke softly to May. "That fat little man in the brown suit, now he's head of the parole board. You don't want to treat him like shit, man. He might remember."

May grimaced. His eyes followed the bustling fat man. "What's his name?"

"Welker. You want me to introduce you so you can shake his hand?"

May took a deep drag of his cigarette and shook his head.

"All right, then," Johnson said. "Put out the butt and get back to work. Why look for trouble?"

May nodded. He took another drag and flipped the butt away. He snapped his fingers. A smaller boy handed him his shovel.

Johnson laughed. "How much you paying him, Dudley?"

"Fuck off, Johnson. If we finish this ditch too soon you'll only find us another one to dig."

"Ain't it the truth," Johnson said grinning. He saw Owen standing and came over. "Okay, what's *your* problem?"

"I was just wondering," Owen said, and then shook his head. "Aw, forget it."

"Let me guess," Johnson said. "You're thinking maybe of running with May's gang when you get out. How's that for mind reading?"

"How you know that?"

"Simple. You got gangs on your head. Hawkins is out. You're not black enough for Dye's Nomads. Santos and Garcia take only Chicanos. So you're thinking May could be the answer to your problem."

He scratched his head, feeling foolish. "Okay. So what's wrong with thinking?"

Johnson wagged his head. "It's not just thinking,

man, it's *that* kind of thinking. Don't you know that when you get out, only two violations will send you back up? One of them's for curfew. The other's for throwing with a gang."

"You mean they're gonna watch me that close?"

"You bet your ass. You've seen McKeon. He's your p.o. man. You think you'll be able to crap McKeon? No way, Kirby. He'll come down on you like a ton, man."

He shrugged. "Okay. Like I said, it was only thinking."

"Fine," Johnson said. "Thinking is the greatest. Only think of something else. Take my word for it, there's a lot you can do outside without joining a gang."

"Yeah, like what?"

Johnson stared down at him. "Like a job. Ever think of that? It's called working for a living."

He grimaced. "Yeah. Only you got to get one. All I learn to do up here is dig a fucking ditch."

"Okay. We'll try you on shop work next week. Maybe you're mechanically minded. You could get on to it here and then try vocational-school training when you get out. You have any objection to being a mechanic?"

"I dunno. I dunno if I can cut it."

"So you take a run at it. See how it goes. What did your old man do? Maybe you've got the same kind of talent."

He picked his words carefully. "I think he used to be a fighter. You know, in the ring."

Johnson pursed his lips. "Well, that's always a way, I guess, if you dig fighting. It's also a good way to get

100

your brains scrambled. That's something you can find out about real easy. When you get back to L.A. just drop into the downtown gym on Main Street."

"What's there?"

"A lot of young fighters training. Working out with their handlers and sparring partners. Exercising. Hitting the bag. Practicing. You'll also see the stumblebums. The old timers who don't know what day it is. What time it is. They walk around punchy." Johnson tapped his skull. "They took too many beatings in the ring."

He wondered if his old man was like that. Rolling around on his heels with the vacant look in his eyes. He had seen them around downtown. Dented noses, scarred eyebrows, ears that looked pounded out of shape. Some of them carried the brown paper bag. Winos. They slept in alleys.

Johnson was appraising him. "You could be some kind of athlete if you take care of yourself and keep working out. But I'll level with you, Owen, that whole fight racket is a sewer. Maybe one out of a hundred makes it. You'd be better off pumping gas or even digging a ditch. I don't know how good your old man was, but if I were you, I'd think an awful lot about it before you decide. Talk to some fellas down at the gym. You'll know."

Owen scowled. "I never said—"

Johnson slapped his shoulder. "I know. I've been running off. Anyway, if I talked you out of it, I'll consider it worthwhile. We'll try to line you up for some work at the garage or electrical stuff. Okay?"

101

He shrugged. Johnson flipped his hand and moved off.

I can pick up trash. Dig a ditch. Clean a toilet. Man, there's lots I can do!

May and the boys around him were smoking and laughing. He walked away, head down. *Who needs 'em. Fuck 'em all!*

That night in his bunk he thought about Bobby Carmona. It was a long trip back to L.A. and he wondered if he'd made it. He wished Carmona hadn't cut out like that. He missed the crazy bastard.

But shit, he's a street cat. I guess he couldn't stand it up here.

Anyway, he told himself, Carmona had the Piratas to go home to. He had nothing.

So I'll sweat it out. It ain't no big deal.

13 The long summer passed. He worked and went to camp school and ate and slept. He played tennis and some ball and learned to fix toilets, light switches, tractors and furniture. The rains came and the drainage ditch he had worked on for so long worked. He felt pretty good about that. He lifted weights and played ping pong and saw movies at the rec hall. He did some paintings on wrapping paper trying to put down the distant mountains the way they were. His colors always turned muddy and he cursed and ripped them up. Then one day Johnson was saying good-by.

"Good-by? Where you going, man?"

"Back to school. You know, this was a summer job."

He was supposed to know that, but he didn't. Maybe he forgot or maybe he didn't want to know.

"Gee, man, well thanks for the tennis."

"No sweat. Next year maybe you'll beat me."

"You coming back?"

"If you cats don't burn down the place. Keep it cool, man. You been doing fine."

Gomez and Brandon said their good-bys, too.

"Jesus, you mean we're gonna be on our own?"

103

Gomez smiled. "No way. They brought in some other social workers. They know their stuff. You'll like them."

"Bullshit."

"Yeah, well try to keep it a happy family. And if I don't see you again, remember what I said."

"What?"

"About gangs."

"Oh, fuck off, Gomez. By the time I get out, I'll be too old for that shit."

"I hope so, for your sake. But you'll be out sooner than you think."

"How come? I still got plenty time to do."

"I heard they need the space. *Adiós, amigo.*"

"Oh, shit. So long, man."

Gomez drew wolf whistles from the Chicanos.

"Don't use it all up in one night, Gomez."

"Yeah. I hope you remember how to use it."

"If you get too much, we'll be glad to fill in for you."

"Fajarse muy bien los calzones, hombre!"

"Behave yourselves, guys," Gomez said. "Maybe I'll see you next year."

They groaned.

The new social workers were introduced. Stuart, Fasco and Barnes. *Shit, who wants them?*

Nobody wanted to bust his ass for the new counselors. It looked like they were right back where they started. Owen felt the change in himself. A hardening. *Man, I think I had it here.*

When Adams called him into his office, he was totally

unprepared for the good news. He was being released. He stared stupidly at the camp director. He hadn't taken Gomez seriously.

Then he was trying to pay attention to what Adams was saying. His mother was sick. Welfare got together with the probation people. His record at camp was good and they thought maybe he could help out at home.

What's she sick about? he wondered.

It would take a few more days to clear everything, Adams said. When all the papers and forms were filled out, McKeon would take him back.

Adams shook his hand. "I've an idea you're going to make it, son. I like the way you've been putting out here. That's all you have to do when you get back home. Keep on putting out. If there's any secret to the whole thing, that's it."

That night in his bunk, he let himself think for the first time about how it would really be. *Sick* meant the booze had caught up with her. He wondered what new crap artist she was shacking up with. There had been so many before he had stopped counting. The only good thing about it was nobody stayed around for too long.

He had to dig real hard to bring back pictures of her together with his old man. The pictures kept fading off. There wasn't any continuity to sustain them. All he saw in his mind's eye was little bits and pieces. Dull growling sounds. A muttered curse from somebody. A

105

chair thrown over. The tape broke a few more times and he figured the hell with it. There was no way he could put it all together.

He counted up his time. A little over eight months. *Shit, that wasn't bad.*

He was called in again when the other boys were off on field duty. Adams smiled. He patted the forms neatly into place. Blue, yellow and white papers.

He looked up and saw McKeon standing inside the door.

He didn't shake hands with Adams again. He didn't say good-by to anybody. He left the same way he came in. All tight inside and a little worried.

McKeon didn't talk much. "I'll ask around. Maybe we can line up a job for you. That's why you're getting off easy, you know. Give you a chance to pull your own weight."

He shrugged. He wasn't making any promises.

"Because if you pick up more trouble," McKeon said, "next time you could wind up in the joint. You wouldn't like that."

The joint was prison. Iron bars and high stone walls. Full security. *You're damn right I wouldn't like it. Maybe you'd have to kill me first to get me in there.*

14

"It's my goddamn liver," she said.

He eyed her fiercely. Sloppy bag. Slack-mouthed vacant face. Watery eyes. Blowzy. Uncombed hair. Beer breath.

Man, she sure ain't no rose.

The housecoat needed buttons. The yellowed slip showed stains. Faded rose-colored house slippers made her feet look swollen.

"Well," she said. "Looks like you're back."

She sat on the sofa. Magazines spilled over the low table. It was dotted with half-empty coffee cups floating cigarette butts. The room had a bad odor. Behind her in the kitchen pots and dishes filled the sink and drainboard.

Man, he thought, this house looks like it ain't been cleaned since Adam was busted and took a fall.

Us fuck-ups at Camp Sawyer, at least we was clean.

He went up the narrow wooden steps. He jerked the bed cover away. His bed was still unmade. Dirty sheet and pillowcase. *Just like you left it, man.*

The window had never been washed. One sock and a shoe were on the floor. He kicked them away. Dust

107

rose. The room was small and held its heat. He went downstairs.

She sat opening a can of beer. "Jesus, it's hot," she said. She drank from the can. "I didn't get a chance to do your room. I wasn't expecting you back so soon."

Yeah, he thought, you got to watch out for that liver. Man, that liver sure must run a trip on you.

He walked outside.

What did you expect, asshole? You been here before.

McKeon had dropped him off at the curb. He came out and needed only one look at the paint-starved house. He stood rooted, legs apart. Busted rocker on the front porch. Dirty windows with drawn shades. The weather-bleached riser boards were warped. The top treads loose. Weeds thrust along the cracked walk. The front lawn sprouted tufts of grass in bare soil. The roof sagged. *Man, that home sweet home is crap.*

The houses on either side didn't look that much better. Junk piled in the yards. Garbage spilled from boxes and cans onto the walk and street. McKeon rubbed his face.

"Give me a call in a couple days. Maybe we can line up some kind of job."

He ain't coming in to see the old lady. He knows.

"You know your way back outta here?"

McKeon nodded. He didn't shake hands or slap his shoulder. He didn't look too happy behind the wheel. He drove off still shaking his head.

The pavement felt strange under his feet. *Man, that is hard.* The sky was covered with a yellow-brown film.

108

His chest felt heavy after walking a single block. He tried not to breathe. His eyes scanned the horizon for mountains.

The trees he noticed were dead.

He walked faster, hating everything he saw, wondering why everybody couldn't wait to get back. To what? he wondered. It wasn't as if any of them had it any better. All the fuck-ups came from neighborhoods like this.

Maybe that's why they got to war in gangs. Maybe it takes their mind off the crap.

Even a big headman like Justin Dye had it like this.

If it ain't as bad, it still ain't no penthouse.

The big sprawling housing project ahead looked like a grim fortress. Hundreds maybe thousands of little windows. Stone walks. Stone playground. Crappy little trees. Kids were playing. Running all over.

He turned away from the project, heading for the freight yards. There would be more space there, fewer people. He wanted suddenly to look at trains.

The yards were deserted. Freight cars lined the rails ahead as far as he could see. Union Pacific. Southern Pacific. Santa Fe. Faded brick-red cars. Cabooses.

He wished he was on one going somewhere.

Where? he asked silently. Where you want to go, jerk?

He shook his head. *I wish to hell I knew.*

East of the area he lived in, the barrio began for the brown-skinned Chicanos. Narrow twisted streets with small frame bungalows fronted by low picket fences.

109

Stunted yucca trees in the front yards. Cheap bars and taco stands. Farther east the tenement housing project encased in concrete walled up hundreds of families. At night there was soft Spanish music from the bungalows. Strumming guitars. Love songs.

People walked the streets talking rapid-fire Spanish. Pretty girls paraded. It was colorful and exciting, like being in another world. *Burritos. Carnitas. Tamales.* It was a barrio where people laughed easily.

The young Chicano street gangs had staked out their own turf. They used scouts and runners. They didn't like visitors. They especially didn't like them looking at their girls. Speaking to one meant trouble. They shot up whities, bloods, their brother Chicanos, anybody who messed with the rules.

Shit, he thought, it ain't worth it.

South was the park where a lot of kids gathered. They popped pills and smoked grass and fights started. Some street gangs used it for their headquarters. The picnic tables were covered with jugs of wine. Vodka. Six-packs.

The black ghetto was farther south and central. They had most of the city gangs. Dye's Nomads were there somewhere, the other side of the park. Maybe ten minutes away.

He wondered if he would ever run into Justin Dye, if Dye would remember him. He thought about the Chicano Carmona.

Sure like to see that little bean again. How's he making out? Them Piratas, man, they must be something else!

110

He felt bigger, stronger as he walked. He had grown some at the camp. Put on more weight. Muscle. Despite the cruddy city air, he felt his blood surging. Being alive. *Some kind of job might do me something. Get me some scratch. I ain't hanging around there looking at her. I wonder if that McKeon was only spinning my wheels about a job. I'm calling that dude first thing tomorrow.*

He started to turn away from the Southern Pacific rail yards. A wide street angled across the rail surface right-of-way. Traffic thundered from the overhead freeway. Cars and trucks kept coming without end.

He stopped. Screaming tires sounded in the short freeway tunnel underpass. An exhaust pipe gurgled with the raspy sound of a broken muffler. He stepped back behind a freight car in the yard.

A car roared out of the tunnel. It cornered fast and bounced over the tracks. He froze. The old air-pitted Pontiac body frame was chopped down low. He could see the tops of their glossy heads. Chicanos. One in the back held a sawed-off shotgun.

His heart hammered suddenly.

The car turned right at the next corner, heading east. The driver was really gunning the old heap. Owen sighed with relief as they passed. Then his head swiveled to the tunnel side again. Another car came roaring out. This one was a green Chevy. The shocks were worn and it bounced over the surface street tracks, rear end scraping and clattering. This car was chopped down, too, and older. He saw the intent dark faces of the boys inside. Blacks.

111

His eyes riveted on the triangular pennant on the antenna. The cloth fluttered. In its center was a triangle painted yellow and rimmed by a thick black circle. He sucked in his breath.

Nomads. White wool stocking hats pulled down to their ears.

The green Chevy careened around the corner, sliding in a tight turn. It fishtailed and then straightened out and roared after the Chicanos in the old white Pontiac. In seconds they were out of sight. He heard shots.

His heart thumped wildly when he stepped out of the yard. *Man, it's like old times.*

If the Nomads didn't catch up with them quickly, they would be in Chicano territory. That wouldn't be very healthy, even for a tough gang like the Nomads. When the bloods or white honkies invaded, a lot of the Chicano gangs came together to fight the common enemy. Whoever was driving the Nomad car had to be crazy not to know. He couldn't imagine Justin Dye wasting his troops that way.

He ran to the corner to follow the action. The gang cars were far down the long street. The lead car faked a left turn and then swerved right abruptly. It disappeared behind buildings, having gained a few yards. The pursuing Nomads cut around after them, trying to close the gap. With only a few more blocks to go before the Chicanos were back in their own turf, he doubted the Nomads would draw blood. Now they would be lucky if they got back healthy. The Chicanos would be after them, this time beefed up by other cars.

112

He listened closely. There were no more shots. He shook his head. It looked like the Nomads blew it.

A breeze came up and loosened his hair. He looked at the darkening sky. There wasn't much time before night. He walked faster. His body pulsed strongly. Shouts and catcalls sounded from the open playground. He stopped.

Cats he knew were playing two-on-one with a red basketball. Charley Bee. Jerry the Jerk. Nick the Knife. They saw him and came over, looking him up and down.

"Hey, man, when you come out?"

"Owen, baby, we heard you was busted, man."

"What can was you at?"

"It wasn't no can, Charley. It was a camp upstate. Camp Sawyer."

"Yeah? How they treat you?"

"Not bad."

"No shit?"

"No shit. It ain't a bad place."

"Oh yeah? What ain't bad about it?"

He thought. "Lots of things. They rap with you. They got good chow. And it was clean, man, you know?"

"Who else was there, anybody from here?"

"They had the Nomad headman Justin Dye."

"Man, I hope you was nice to him."

"Oh, he wasn't no trouble. He was regular."

"Who else?"

"Some jerk Hawkins. Runs the Tips."

"Tips? They ain't much."

113

"Well you asked."

"Who else?"

"Some bean from the Piratas."

"The Piratas? Who?"

"Some kid called Carmona."

"What's he like?"

He couldn't help smiling. "Don't pick no fights with him. He busted up Hawkins at nearly twice his weight."

"No shit?"

"I ain't crapping you. Man, he is fast." He shadow-boxed for them, throwing fast punches in the air. One-two. One-two-three. Carmona's lightning.

"Anybody else?"

"There was Santos and Garcia, two big Chicano headmen. And there was this cat from the Hollywood Blues—their headman May. He didn't say much. He was waiting it out like Dye."

Charley Bee looked down at his feet. He kept his voice low. "You're back quick, man. You running?"

"I was let go. I done eight months of the two years."

"How come?"

"They tol' me my old lady was sick. They wanted me home to help out."

They exchanged glances.

"She says it's her liver," he said, watching them grin. They all knew about his old lady.

"My old man needed an operation to fix that," Jerry said. "They cut the bar rail out from under his foot."

"Yeah," he said. "That's a good way."

Jerry said, "The trouble is, he's got two feet. He

114

knows it's gonna kill him but he don't give a shit."

He thought about it killing her. She didn't look all that sick. She could have been a junkie like some of the others and been worse off. Nick's old lady was a mainliner. She had tracks on her arm you wouldn't believe.

"Who's your p.o.?" said Jerry.

"McKeon."

"That fat ass!"

He shrugged. "McKeon's okay."

"Wait till you bust your parole. You see how okay he is. Like all them other motherfuckin' chickenshit p.o.'s."

He remembered Jerry had done a few years at Camarillo when he was younger for setting fire to his own house. "What you guys doing later?"

"The same shit," Charley said.

He turned. "Okay. I'll see you later tonight."

Nick smiled. "It's your own ass, man."

"Yeah. So fuck it."

They went back to the game. He heard the ball dribbling from down the street. They were cursing, screaming and laughing. He passed an outdoor fruit and vegetable stand. He looked down and there was an apple in his hand.

The owner came running out in his white linen coat. He shook his fist, yelling something.

Owen was running, biting into the apple. Laughing. *Looks like I'm home.*

115

15 The slanting early-morning sun stirred him awake. He didn't remember the small room. Where was everybody? His eyes found a familiar object and he knew. His head throbbed. The wine was sweet and sticky in his throat. He felt dull and listless. He stared unwinking at the ceiling. Motes moved in the bright yellow sun rays, spinning slowly.

He stretched and saw his shirt. He had not bothered to undress. His stomach growled. *Man, that wine is shit.*

Camp Sawyer seemed another time zone. He woke up clear-headed. Bouncing out of bed to the cold morning air, the breath-taking cold outdoor shower. Yelling and slapping at himself. Comparing dicks. Body tingling as he hurried to breakfast at the chow hall.

Owen sat up. The room spun. He felt nausea, like puking. *Man, I'll have to get used to this all over again.*

Her stockings and bra and underwear were hanging all over the bathroom. Like moist steamy vines on the shower curtain pipe. *Fuck it.* He took a leak and threw tepid water on his face. Downstairs the living room reeked of her beer.

An open can of tuna was molding in the refrigerator.

The container of milk was lumpy and sour. He slammed the door and went outside. A few blocks away he found the milk delivery truck. The driver was across the street in the tenement. Owen opened the door and reached inside. He picked up a carton of milk and a box of eggs. He stood there and let two eggs slide down his throat. He dropped the box on the street. He opened the milk container, put his head back and gulped greedily. He drank nearly half and threw the rest away while he was walking. He found a crumpled cigarette in his pocket and lit up.

The neighborhood was still asleep. All the stores were locked up tight. He rummaged in the storage bin behind one. Squashed oranges. Brown, leaking, overripe bananas. He dumped them back and kept digging. He found some grapes and an apple with soft brown spots. He bit out the spots and spit them away. He heard a soft sound. A cat hung poised on the fence, staring down. "It's all yours," he said. The cat waited. He threw the apple at it. The cat disappeared.

He jogged to the park. Morning traffic thundered on the freeway. The air hung heavy and acrid, stinging his eyes. He could see the bare foothills of Pasadena beyond the brown haze. There were white houses along the sides of the mountains.

He had been to Pasadena. It was pretty neat—rich dudes—but the air was really crap. Worse than here. Some days you couldn't see the white houses or the mountains.

The neighborhood park was deserted. Refuse littered

the grass and picnic tables. Beer cans. Empty wine and vodka bottles. White Satin. Dapple. Muscatel. Sweet wine went with smoking pot or popping pills. He found a jug and tilted it. The wine left was sour.

The grass was wet with morning dew. He explored among the white boxes. Most of the chicken bones were gnawed clean. He found one with some meat left and chewed. He went among the taco boxes and wax paper. He found some crumbs and then enough vodka left in a fifth for a swallow.

He swept the debris off a long green picnic table and lay down. Tree branches and leaves blotted most of the sky. He stared up the lacy pattern and fell asleep.

He woke up with the heat of the morning. Winos were coming into the park. They would be going through every jug and bottle. Kids came marching in with teacher groups. They were released and started bouncing and screaming.

Jesus! His head hurt.

He walked away. His body dragged. He slapped at his sides. *Man, you been back only one day and already your ass is dragging.*

It must be the hours, he thought. You put in longer hours here. Yeah, it's got to be the hours. I mean, what the fuck—we didn't do anything. Horsed around. Smoked. Put down some wine. Shit, that ain't so bad.

He picked up with his old crowd as if he hadn't been away. They sat around drinking Charley's wine. The first butt felt heavy after so long. After a few, he was used to it. *Anyway, what the fuck—it's something to do.*

They watched the park fill up. It was a warm night and nobody was going to miss any of the action. A gang of black dudes came roaring up on big Harley choppers. Satin Devils. A chapter of the Hell's Angels, somebody said. They weren't kids. They wore black caps and purple basketball shirts with orange trimming. A few had thick silver bracelets on their bare arms. They didn't have their old ladies with them.

He thought they would take over the action in the park. Instead they sat astride their cycles smoking, looking over the scene. Then abruptly they revved up and roared away.

"One of them took on five Nomads here a couple weeks ago," Charley said.

"Yeah?" Owen said. "What happened?"

"They beat the crap outta him."

Later they walked downtown and went into an all-night movie. The place stank. A lot of the derelicts spent the night here. He'd done it many times himself.

"There's one queer here you got to see," Jerry said. "He's got long blond hair. When he finds somebody, you'd think it was a fella necking with a girl."

They looked for the queers and tapped each other knowingly whenever one changed seats and moved in on a single. They did it quietly and seemed to know what they were doing. Nobody yelled or got pissed off.

The features were old scratched prints of Westerns. Nobody paid attention to the screen. People slept and

119

snored. A drunk behind them broke wind loudly. It cracked them up. They went upstairs, wrote on the urinal walls and left laughing.

A few blocks away from the movie house they saw an old wino shuffling along. His long overcoat nearly covered the baggy trousers. He moved along aimlessly.

"Let's tap him," Charley said. "Maybe he's got some panhandling money."

At the next alley, Charley bumped him inside. Jerry and Nick jumped him as he was stumbling. Owen watched. The old man didn't move when they had him flat on his back.

They turned his pockets inside out. There was nothing. The old man's toothless jaws worked. His gaping mouth frothed with pink spittle. He made little sounds like a bird.

Well shit, he thought. If we don't do it, the next guys do.

A police siren sounded close. They ran up the alley, still laughing. When he looked back, the old wino was still on his back. His arms flailed the air. He looked helpless like a turtle. *Shit*, he thought. *How did Gomez and Johnson get out?*

He looked up now. The building was very old. The weather-beaten sign over the doorway hung warped. Main Street Gym.

Hey, how about that? he said to himself. I guess this place was on my mind.

A sign hung on the door. Admission Fifty Cents.

120

Nobody was paying. He walked inside. He blinked at dim top lights. The place was barnlike. It was morning and it already smelled of sweat and liniment and freshly mopped floors.

Men stood in clusters, watching. Cigars and cigarettes jutted from their mouths. They looked old and serious. Two fighters moved swiftly in a boxing ring over his head. They were short and squat. One wore thick leather headgear to cover his brows and ears. Stenciled on the back of his short-sleeved shirt was Chico Carasco. The other Chicano was stripped above the waist. His muscular body gleamed with perspiration. There were red patches where he had been hit.

Carasco extended his arms and they touched gloves. "Let's go, Valdez," Carasco said.

Their fighting shoes rasped on the canvas floor of the ring. They glided apart and came together. The punches were loud like pistol shots. His own body twitched in miniature response to their bobbing and weaving. When they punched, his arms tightened. They worked fast, businesslike. Feint. Lead and parry. Stick and move. Most of the punches were blocked by their forearms. Carasco wore a mouthpiece. It didn't fit his jaws. He had trouble breathing.

Sounds came from far across the large gym. Owen turned to see another ring with fast-moving shadowy figures. There was a quick blurring movement and a fast thudding series of blows. He saw Carasco's opponent reel off-balance and go down to his haunches. His eyes looked startled.

121

A man waved a folded newspaper, shouted short words. The fighter shook his thick black hair and bounced up. He pounded his gloves together, wiped them on his black trunks. There wasn't a referee in the ring.

Carasco came at Valdez in a smooth gliding movement and then punched very hard and fast, opening his shoulders. The other was driven back against the ropes. He cradled his face behind his thick arms, covering up, absorbing the blows on his gloves and forearms. Carasco's flurry ended and Valdez went in himself, throwing long punches. A short left hook stopped Valdez short. Carasco hammered at his body with heavy thuds. Then he hooked Valdez again and crossed his right. As the other fell, Carasco spit out his mouthpiece.

Valdez rolled to his knees. Up close, he looked very young. A whistle sounded. He spit blood on the canvas. He got up and followed Carasco to the same corner. Carasco patted his shoulder. Valdez looked disgusted.

Carasco laughed. He wasn't that much older. His arms were thin and frail-looking compared to the other.

He remembered Carmona.

A man in the corner dabbed white ointment over Valdez's eye. He winced. The handler spoke in fast, flowing Spanish to both. He pantomimed several times, protecting the right ear when he threw his left. The Mexican-American fighters stood together, appearing not to listen. Their chests heaved and they gulped for air.

122

They ducked out between the ropes and two young blacks came in. They were tall and thin, maybe light-weights. They were awkward and grinning self-consciously. They didn't know how to fight. Owen watched them miss at long range and moved off.

That Chico Carasco was pretty good, he thought. He felt the thickness of his own arms. He walked from the crowd to the edges of the place. Fighters were training, punching the bags, doing sit-ups, skipping rope. They were black, brown and white. A few older ones were thickset and carried flab.

Big white canvas bags hung from the ceiling rafters. He stepped in close to one. He punched it hard. There wasn't much of a sound and his hand hurt. *That mother's made of iron.* He walked around the heavy sandbag suspiciously. Then he came in close and punched at it with both fists. The bag sagged some. His fists stung and felt raw. His arms ached.

Well, fuck that!

A stout man was watching him. "Hey, kid, you fixing to be a fighter?"

He shook his head. "Shit, no."

The man nodded without expression, chewing on the stub of his cigar, and turned away. Owen heard thudding sounds. A heavy man was hitting one of the big bags. He was really punishing it. The bag danced when hit. The man was wearing thin gloves. Owen felt odd inside. He wondered if this was how his old man got started.

He looked back at the fighters in the ring. Circling.

Hitting. Getting hit. All around the place they were working out, grunting. He heard a rapid fire of sharp staccato sounds.

A fighter was hitting the light bag with perfect timing. He kept it moving in a steady beat with lefts and then rights. The bag became a blur.

That don't look easy.

A middle-aged stocky man came by with a rolling gait. He waved his hand to the fighter punching the light bag. His voice was hoarse, throaty. "Atta boy. Keep punchin', kid."

The fighter punching the bag stepped back. His T-shirt was stained with sweat. He smiled to the man. "Hey, how you doin', champ?"

The stocky man wagged his head, dropped it between his lifted shoulders. He moved his fists. "Okay. We're doin' okay. We're gonna take him, kid. You watch."

Owen saw the scar tissue ridges over the man's eyes. The nose was battered shapeless. Cauliflower ears curled grotesquely. A light gleamed briefly in the pale blue eyes. He began grinning widely. He saw Owen. The eyes turned vacant. He waved a big fist. The knuckles were huge and worn smooth. "Ya know what?" he said. "Ya know what?" He blinked and lost the thread. "Yeah. Okay, Marty. We do that." He walked off, mumbling to himself.

Punchy. The guy's punchy.

Owen looked closely at the young guy punching the light bag. He looked in his twenties and his face was

124

unmarked. *Maybe he ain't had a fight yet,* he thought. *Maybe he's only working out to get ready.*

The young guy gave the bag a final hard blow with his right and stepped back. He pulled his T-shirt off and tossed it aside. He began doing sit-ups on the mat. His arms were long and muscular. His stomach muscles stood out thick like ropes.

"Hey," Owen said, "was that punchy guy really a champ?"

The fighter paused as he came up, hands locked behind his head. "Who, Barry? Sure. He was middleweight champ. Back some years—maybe fifteen, twenty. Red Barry."

Owen waited another dozen sit-ups. "Was he any good?"

Dark eyes met his, looking puzzled, almost angry. "Good? What'cha mean *good?* He was champ, wasn't he? Maybe four or five years he beat everybody. One thing Barry had, he could take a punch."

"Okay. Thanks."

He watched the lithe muscular body rise, twisting, and fall back, twist up forward again. He looked like he could go another fifty without tiring.

I wonder if he ever heard of J. C. Kirby, he thought.

He didn't want to ask. Maybe the old-timer—the champ—might know.

He watched the light-haired stocky man moving away. *What would he know, jerk?* he said to himself. *His brains are scrambled.*

It came over him suddenly. He wished he knew if

his old man ever was any good. He watched the young guy going. Did he train like this? he wondered. Could he hit? Take a punch? Was he fast—quick with his hands—like Carmona?

Balls, he thought, forget it. You'll never know and anyway, what's the difference?

At one side of the gym were small card tables. There were old sporting magazines. He picked up a copy of *Ring News*. There were pictures of fighters inside. Did his old man look like that? he wondered. Standing tough in fighting pose, left hand out, right cocked and ready.

He flipped through columns of won-lost records. No J. C. Kirby here, man. He checked the cover date. It was two years old. He looked for others. The oldest he found was five years old. He went through it anyway and tossed it aside.

He wasn't around then, jerk. What you expect?

He passed the stout man with the cigar in his mouth.

Hey, you ever hear of a fighter J. C. Kirby?

What'd he fight at?

Middleweight.

Lemme think. . . .

Fuck it, he told himself. He left before the fat man had a chance to think, and remembered his old man was a bum.

16 He put off calling Mc-
Keon. One more day, one more day, he kept telling
himself. Shit, man, look how long you been away!

He felt out of tune, awkward with his old buddies.
Like he came down from another planet suddenly, he
thought. Jesus, everybody else is the same. Shit, what
happened?

I guess rolling old winos just ain't funny no more.

The old lady stank from beer or wine or booze. His
room stank. The house stank. The whole goddamn city
stank.

*It must be my nose. Something's wrong with my
fucking nose.*

The trouble was Gomez and Johnson and Camp Sawyer were still with him and he couldn't shake them
loose. He knew it but he didn't want to think about it.

*Well, shit, it was only eight months. That ain't too
long a time.*

Charley and Nick were into running soft drugs. Barbs
and grass. Amphetamines and cocaine. They had a
good connection and made out. Jerry lifted anything
that wasn't nailed down. He stole bikes, TV sets, type-
writers, adding machines. Sometimes Charley and Nick

127

made a bill a week. Jerry got five percent off the selling price.

Nobody said anything. They were waiting for him to come around. Sometimes he thought they were looking at him.

Like I'm a queer, he thought.

"Them office buildings are a panic," Jerry said. "Shit, you just walk in lunchtime and you got all you can take."

He told Jerry that was great and he was still looking.

"Well, yeah, but shit, man, you got to get into something."

How did you get out, Gomez? he asked silently. What's the secret?

Maybe if I tie into a gang it'll give me something to do.

They were all around. Running loose. Acting cool like everybody was afraid of them. The fuzz looked the other way.

On my own, I'd get busted first shot.

There were the fighting gangs and the other kind that robbed the merchants or had a steady take every week for protection.

Maybe I can work up my own business, he thought. All I need is a couple customers who don't want no trouble.

Big Johnson roared inside his head. "Man, that is crap! What is wrong with your head? There is only one way you can go. Out. You got to go *out!*"

128

Oh, fuck off, Johnson, he said wearily. Get off my back.

He clenched his fists and turned them over and looked at them closely. They were good-sized, but he remembered the hugeness of the old punchy ex-champ Barry's. Jesus, they were really weapons, he thought. Like fucking rocks.

The dude there, the young fighter training, said Barry could take a punch. *Yeah, it sure did him a lot of good. They only punched his brains out.*

Maybe that's what happened to his old man, he thought. Maybe he caught so many in the head he didn't know what he was doing.

But Barry made champ, he told himself. There's a difference.

Only he wouldn't know it now if you told him about it. So what good was it?

Owen felt old and tired. His head hurt. He shook his arms and hands loose. Come on, he urged himself silently. What the fuck. Don't worry. It'll all work out.

Johnson smiled inside his head. "That's what I said. Out. That's how you do it. You cut out."

He shook his head and started to jog down the long street. After a while, his muscles loosened and he ran with easier, longer strides. He was a machine eating up the distance. The street rolled by beneath him.

Anyway, he told himself, you run good. So it ain't a total loss.

He was running so good he never saw the car tailing

129

him. He heard its bubbling exhaust at the next corner, but it was too late then. He turned his head and saw the kid in the back with the sawed-off shotgun on him, and he stopped.

The driver swung the car in close to the curb expertly. It was a black T-Bird, maybe ten years old, with the finish scratched and a dented right fender. The windshield had two bullet holes and was cracked high on the driver's left side. The front bumper hung low on the curb side.

Maybe that driver ain't so hot, he thought, and then he noticed the small piece of cardboard tied to the center bolt. It was hand-lettered in black paint. Mongols.

His legs trembled. *Who the fuck are the Mongols?*

The driver stayed behind the wheel. The kid holding the shotgun stayed put. Three others got out. They came at him from the far side so the kid with the shotgun could do something if he got cute.

The street was only three blocks away from the police station. It was four o'clock in the afternoon. There was a tavern down the street about forty yards away. A feed store was next to it, and then a small grocery. Behind him was an empty lot that didn't go anywhere. If he ran for the lot, that's where they would find his body.

His ears strained for the sound of a cruising prowl car. His eyes rolled fast to their limits and he didn't see anything. Fucking fuzz, he thought. If it was me doing the rip-off, they'd be all over the place.

They were about his age, maybe younger. The three

130

on the street wore faded jeans and sneakers and T-shirts. The shirts were white with a big design covering the front. It looked like a rattlesnake coiled around a bolt of lightning.

What the fuck's that got to do with Mongols? his mind asked.

The kid nearest him looked nervous. He pulled out a switchblade knife and poked it out, stiff-armed. His voice quivered more than the blade.

"All right, man, what'cha got? You got some joy-poppers on you?"

Owen shook his heard. The nervousness worried him. "No. I ain't no junkie. I got nothin'."

The two behind the nervous thin one ducked their heads and whispered to him. As he listened, his eyes rolled. He wagged the knife blade back and forth stiffly.

"All right, all right. What about some juanita? Grass."

"I don't dig that either. If you want—"

The blade wavered in front of his face again and he clammed up. They whispered something else and stepped aside to cover him in case he broke. One of them pulled out a beer-can opener. The third held a corkscrew. His eyes froze on the strange weapon and he winced inwardly. *Jesus!*

"All right, man." Switchblade took a step forward and Owen could smell his breath. Sweet wine. "You got some bread, let's have it. It's your last chance."

"Right here," he said, afraid to move his arms. His chin bobbed to the pocket on the left side of his chest. "You want to take it out or you want me?"

131

"I'll do it," the kid said. "You better not try nothin'."

He shook his head mutely. The kid came in with the knife cocked high in his right hand. His left leg advanced under his extending left arm. The hand came closer and Owen froze and held his breath as the shaking fingers touched him.

In his mind, he clamped the kid's hand to his chest, pinning it there. He threw his right hand against the kid's chin. The blow shattered him and he crumbled to the pavement. He whirled and took out the second kid with the beer-can opener by kicking him in the balls. The light-haired kid with the corkscrew was the one he really wanted. He wanted to hurt that one with that fucking corkscrew.

The hand came out of his shirt pocket and drew back with the crumpled soggy bills wrapped around some change. He handed it over his shoulder to the others. "Okay. Count it," he said.

The second one took it and opened it up. The kid with the switchblade squared off at him again, ready to spring, it looked. "It's all I got," he said.

"Seven fifty-two," the other kid said. "It's okay."

The kid with the blade nodded and gulped. "Okay. Fuck around now and you get this." He backed off warily, holding the blade out. The others scurried behind him and got the car doors open. The kid with the shotgun was grinning.

They got in the car and the doors slammed. The driver gunned the engine and the old heap bucketed away. It spun and fishtailed, and Owen smelled the stripped rubber.

He stood there watching the car head down the street. At the next corner, it turned left. That's a good move, he said. Now they're gonna rip off the fucking police station.

His arms felt cold, and when he rubbed them he saw the goose flesh. His legs were still trembling. He could still smell the wine on the kid's breath, see his shaking hand and the glinting switchblade. Then he remembered the corkscrew, and shuddered.

He hit his hand angrily and went to his pocket. There wasn't anything left.

Fuckin' assholes, he thought. I bet I was their first rip-off.

A black and white prowl car came nosing into the same corner the kids had taken in the T-Bird. It turned right and slowly came his way down the street. He stood there with his hands on his hips. The driver looked him over as he came up and he stared back, unwinking. The driver lifted his hand in greeting.

Up yours, Jack, he thought. Where the fuck were you two minutes ago?

He followed the car with angry eyes until it was out of sight. Then he sighed and began to walk back slowly.

Come on, Gomez, he said, jeering. Tell me some more.

He kicked the pavement and said aloud, "Shit!"

17

"There was only three of them?" Charley said. "Shit, why'n't you do somethin'?"

"Like what?" he said. "You're forgettin' there's this cat in the back of the car with the double-barreled shotgun."

"So shit, what if it ain't loaded?"

"I thought of that. Then I also thought like what if it was?"

"What about the driver?" Nick said. "What was he holding?"

Jerry whipped his hand fast. "Probably his meat. Shit, he hadda be doin' somethin', didn't he?"

He watched Charley laughing with Jerry.

"Tell you the truth, what scared me, what scared me the most, was they was so nervous. Like it was their first rip-off. Shit, I didn't know what they'd do."

Charley shook his head. "I never heard of no Mongols. Where the fuck they from?"

"Beats me. That's what I thought. I never heard of no fucking Mongols neither."

He had asked around later. Nobody knew about the Mongols gang.

134

"Maybe they're from outta the city. You check the plates?"

"No," he said. "I forgot to look. I just took it for granted they was from around here someplace."

"Well, I ain't never heard of no fuckin' Mongols from no place."

"Yeah. Well, thanks."

"If we see 'em around, we'll let you know, man."

"My last seven bucks," he said now. "Them fuckin' bastards got it. And what really burns my ass is, they didn't seem to know what the fuck they was doing." He shrugged and shook his head. "But I wasn't going to argue with no switchblade and shotgun. Not to mention this jerk with the corkscrew. A corkscrew, for Crissakes, you ever hear of that? Can you imagine anybody taking a piece outta you with a fucking corkscrew?"

"I wouldn't argue with that neither," Jerry said. "That fucker would take a big chunk outta you, it would. Jesus! I'd shit in my pants."

"Yeah," he said. "To tell the truth, I wasn't so far from it. And two minutes later, wouldn't you know, the fuzz comes around the block and looks me over."

"Maybe you oughtta forget it," Nick said. "Like it just wasn't your day. We'll catch up to 'em sometime."

"Yeah," he said. It kept running around in his head. A phonograph record with the needle stuck in its track. *Goddamn Mongols. Five assholes that didn't know their ass from first base. And they take me out.*

It could have been the Nomads, or the Sinners, the

135

Piratas, the Pharaohs—any of those—and he'd have felt lucky to still be alive and in one piece. But these assholes—Jesus! They set up that sawed-off shotgun in the back with the damn thing trained on your ass, and what are you going to do—argue with them?

He played it over and over again in his mind, and he still didn't see how he could have avoided being ripped off. The goddamn fuzz were near enough, but there was no way he could have stalled, hoping they'd come around the corner in time to save his ass.

With that goddamn corkscrew staring me inna face, for Crissakes? What the hell was that asshole hoping to do with the fuckin' corkscrew? Jesus!

His mind somehow rejected the reality and menace of the switchblade knife and the beer-can opener. The living thought of the corkscrew and what it might have done bugged him.

I get that corkscrew dude one day, I'm really gonna stomp the bastard.

He looked around at them. "Shit, now I really gotta do something. I need some bread."

Charley smoked. He thought about it. "Well, you can come in with us, you know. We got a good connection."

"No, Charley," he said. "No thanks. I don't want no part of that shit. I don't want to hustle no drugs, you don't mind. I'll find something."

"It ain't no worse than the other shit," Charley said. "What's the difference it's drugs?"

"I wish I knew what the fuck it was, Charley. All I

136

know is I fuckin' don't like it, you know? But thanks, anyway. I'll look around."

"You might look up Pete," Nick said.

"Who's Pete?"

"He's into a lotta things."

"So where do I find him, I'm interested?" he said.

"He sits in a big white El D," Jerry said. "Out front the phone on Romaine, corner Longo. Big fat cat."

"Well, maybe," he said, "maybe I'll drop around. I'll think about it."

"Pete pays you right off," Jerry said. "He don't fuck you around."

"Okay, so how come you don't do work for him, he's so reliable?" he said.

"It's the percentage, man," Charley said. "Pete gives you five off his take. We do better with our shit. But we do a job for him sometime, when our shit ain't movin'."

"White El D," he said. "On Romaine, out the phone by Longo."

"Big fat cat," Jerry said.

He thought about it on the way. *It won't hurt to look. It ain't like I got to take anything. What I need is some kind of action so I stay alive. If he's okay, we work it out, so long as I don't get stiffed.*

The man sat behind the wheel of the long white El Dorado Caddy. It was washed and clean. The blue and orange license plate read California 123 PTB. It was a late model.

137

The phone booth stood open. He walked to the corner and back. The man was smoking a cigar, reading a newspaper.

The window on his side rolled down. "Hey, you."

"Yeah?"

"C'mere."

Owen stepped closer. The man was thickset, swarthy. His white shirt was open at the throat. His skin looked oily.

"You live around here?" the man said.

"Yeah." The fat man wore neat tan pants.

"Where around here?"

"Tuero Street."

"Okay, so what'cha doin' here—you checkin' me out?"

He shrugged. "You Pete?"

The man leaned forward. He pressed a button and pushed the door open. "Siddown."

Owen hesitated. The fat man's sports jacket lay folded.

"Come in and siddown," the man said. "I ain't no queer. We wanna talk, don't we?"

Owen pulled the door open wider and slid in. He pulled it shut. The man tapped a button. It clicked and the door locked. Another button and the window rolled up silently.

The man grinned. He looked fat and friendly. He had rings on both hands. One was thick gold. The other was a sparkling star sapphire. "Okay, so we talk," he said. "You wanna leave, you lift the button on the door. Okay?"

138

"Okay."

"What's your name, kid?"

"Kirby. Owen Kirby."

"You done time?"

He looked at the man.

"Look, kid, let's not fart around. We work together, I wanna know what I got goin' for me onna line. You been busted, I wanna know for what and how many. My kind of action, I got to pick, I don't want to make no wrong guesses."

"I just did eight months up at Camp Sawyer."

"Camp Sawyer? Where the fuck is Camp Sawyer? I never heard no Camp Sawyer."

"Upstate. It's pretty new, I guess. A new idea, anyway."

"Yeah? So what's so new about it?"

"No guards, no fences. Like that."

The man grinned. "No shit? You just leave when you fuckin' feel like?"

He shrugged again. For some reason, he didn't like bad-mouthing the camp. "Anyway," he said, "not too many did."

"Okay, okay. So you dug the place, okay. What was you up for? Come on, kid, we gotta level, you wanna connect."

"I was jumped by a couple dudes. I cut some of them up. I got two years. They cut it short. I only just come back."

"That's okay," the man said. "Comes down to it, you got self-defense. You got a gun?"

139

He shook his head.

"That's smart," the man said. "I don't like no shootin'. Somethin' goes wrong, you fuck up, you eat it, see? You don't go crazy. You take the fall. Okay?"

"Well," Owen said, "well, sure. Only it's gotta be worth it. Next time I might luck out. I hear there's lots worse than Camp Sawyer I was at."

"Yer fuckin' right, there's worse. There's lots worse. What you drew there, you know, it sounds like a piece a cake. Right? So now yer here, I'll fill you in. Yer innerested, we go ahead. You want out, okay, there's no shortage kids like you wanna make a fast buck, you dig?"

Johnson was trying to get into his head, trying to tell him something. *Fuck off, Johnson,* he said silently, wagging his head side to side. *It's my ass.*

"Sure," he told the man. "I dig. Only so far I ain't heard nothin'."

"That's right," the man said. "You ain't heard nothin' on account of I ain't told you nothin'. You're down here, you maybe know my kinda action. What we do, we do hard goods. I pick a place, I tell you what we need, you go in and take it out. You with me, Kirby?"

"Like what kinda hard goods?" he said.

"Like color TV. Stereos. Record changers. That kinda shit."

He could see himself on the street, a color TV under one arm, a stereo set in the other, dragging his ass with the load, and then the siren in his ears and the search-

140

light blinding his eyes, him trying to run, to move, to get the hell out of there.

"Them color TVs," he said. "Those are big bastards, ain't they?"

"Nah," the man said. "I'm talkin' only portables. They weigh maybe forty, fifty pounds. You look like a strong kid, it's no big deal somebody your built."

"Yeah, okay," he said. "Only how far do I take the mothers? If I was to take the bastards out, where do I hafta take 'em?"

The man laughed. He had large white teeth, very evenly spaced. His voices was raspy but it went with the way he looked and his kind of action. His wristwatch was pale, thin gold.

"First you gotta say if yer in or what," he said. "If I tell every horse's ass what comes along what we do and how we do it, we'd be outta business the first guy shoots off his lip."

"You didn't tell me my end," he said. "If it's my ass, I gotta know if it's worth, you know."

"Five," the man said. "You get five percent offa what we sell the merchandise for."

"Yeah," he said, "only I don't know what, I mean, gimme an idea what one operation does me, okay?"

"This one I got in mind, you want in, you do a bill."

"A hunnerd bucks?"

"We get the goods, you get the hunnerd. You don't wait till we make the sale. You get paid up front—on delivery. Okay?"

141

He thought about it. Behind the phone booth was a small one-story taxpayer over a store. Nuys Hardware. Next to it was an old two-story tenement. There were pots with dead plants on the sills of the windows. The windows were grimed and dirty. The stoop and side-walk separated low, withered hedges. The sky looked dead. Flat, washed-out blue with streaks of brown and yellow. A bird flashed down. It lit on the hedge and moved its bill. The sound was muffled by the rolled-down window, but he thought it would be harsh and rasping.

"Hey, look—that's a bluejay."

"No shit," the fat man said. "That fuckin' bird, you mean?"

"Yeah. We had 'em up there." He rubbed his nose.

"You gotta shit or get offa the pot, kid," the man said. "What'll it be? You want it or not?"

"I was just thinking," he said. "This is a night job, right?"

The man looked at him. "No," he said, "we just drop in from the roof the middle of the day and tell the customers to move their asses outta the way so we can take the goods out."

"I mean," Owen said, "I dig the idea being paid right off. But say I'm stopped. They look me over at one in the morning and I got a big bill on me, and they got to pull me in and ask how I got it."

"No problem," the man said. "I'm here every day in front the hardware. You come by next day, it's here for you."

142

He looked at the fat man.

The fat man shook his head, opened his window and threw out his cigar. "Open the glove," he said.

Owen blinked. "Oh," he said. He opened the glove compartment. The lid came down and he saw more bills than he had ever seen in his life. They were stacked and piled together and filled the foot-long, deep compartment.

"Okay. Shut the glove," the man said. He pushed the lid back up. "What day is today?"

"Huh? It's Thursday, I think."

"Goddamn right. Thursday's payoff day. Like nearly every other day. The kids come along for their take, it's here, the money's here, on the line. Now you wanna pick yours up tomorrow, it'll be here, same way."

"Okay," he said. "I think that's better for me. Okay, Pete. I'm in."

The fat man reached for his coat pocket and pulled out a paper. He smoothed out the folds over his knee. He pointed to a penciled diagram of a building.

"Now here's how we do it," the fat man said.

18 At twelve-fifteen on a dark gusty night with a touch of light drizzling rain, Owen Kirby went over the blacktop roof of the block of two-story red brick buildings on his way to hit Sherm's TV and Stereo. He was wearing dark blue jeans and sneakers and an old sweat shirt. He had gone in the first building on the corner of Main and Second through the back door opening to the parking lot. The door was padlocked and he picked the lock with a sharp long nail. He closed the door carefully behind him and hoped no guards would come nosing through the alley running behind the block of buildings and notice the lock was missing. He had to come through the back because the fat man had told him the front door was wired to a silent alarm.

He went up the stone steps of the darkened building to the top and found the roof door. The padlock on this one was old and rusted and he was able to twist the sliding shackle loose and off the hasp holding it. He opened the door and stepped out on the roof.

The roof extended across the three buildings, separated only by low white concrete-block walls. He stepped lightly over the black tar roofing paper, feeling

144

it crackle under his feet. He climbed easily over the low line of brick-capped concrete blocks and made the second roof. The night was misty, the rain soft on his face. He looked across the street and liked the effect of the mist and rain and the street lights on Denny's, the towering fifteen-story department store fronting the entire block. It looked silent and still and formidable, the fog drifting around it, like the mountains he remembered upstate around Camp Sawyer.

He shook off the feeling and went across the second block barrier. He felt a little nervous and sweaty but not as much as he expected. Doing it alone made it a harder bit but gave him the edge he needed.

"You can do it alone," the fat man had said, "or cut somebody in you know. I'd hafta know who you was bringin', of course, so I'd know. But you don't need nobody, and this way you don't have nobody to cut in, I mean, you go solo."

He thought of Charley or Jerry and Nick. But they had their own action going. Also, this way he wouldn't have to split the bill he got two or three ways, and the job would carry him a while.

"If I was using," he told the fat man, "I'd ask Charley Bee or Jerry Jerkis. You know them. They done work for you. But I think, shit, I'll handle it myself."

He went halfway across the last building and lifted the rooftop cap off the skylight behind the stairwell. It was stuck tight and he had to work it and hit the edges up hard with the heels of his hands. Before he

145

went down the single-rung iron ladder, he pulled the cap over and dropped it back in place.

So far, so good, he told himself. If you don't fuck up, this oughtta be a piece a cake. I wouldn't mind more like it.

There was a dim white bulb high overhead. He went down the narrow stone steps behind the vertical iron ladder. He looked back up when he got to the bottom and saw the black wet tracks his sneakers had made.

Well, shit, he thought, it ain't like fingerprints, every asshole I know wears sneakers, so what'll it tell them?

He came to the door. He put his hand in his pocket and fingered the key.

"This key," the fat man said, "oughtta do it. If it don't, then I been fucked. You go out the same way you come in, and I'll give you twenty for your time. Deal?"

Why not, he thought, he'd still be ahead for nearly nothing.

"Another thing," the fat man said, "if it works like it should, don't become a smart ass when you get down there. You take from the back left wall as you come in. Only what's on the floor and the rear counter. Nothing else, I don't give a shit it's diamonds."

"Okay. How come if I see something better?"

The fat man tapped his chest with a stubby forefinger. "Because, shithead, we take only what the man buys back."

He looked at the fat man.

The man laughed. "It's okay, you're young, you'll get smart. How come I can pay you a bill up front when

146

you only get five? How do I know I'll make the two Gs?"

"Well, yeah," he said, "I was like wondering myself."

The stubby finger jabbed his chest again. He felt it thump on his bone there. "Because the man gives me a price to buy it back already, asshole. It's insurance money, you dig? It's a heist, sure, but the man calls it himself. He collects on the insurance money and buys it back for a price, and makes himself a little, and we all make a little. Okay?"

"Oh," he said, "for Christ sake."

The fat man grinned. "That's why you got to bust in. He can't leave no doors open, see? After you use the key, you run a wire through the fuckin' lock, so it looks, you know?"

The key was a dupe, he thought, because it fit in easy. The tumblers moved and he cautiously worked the door open. He remembered the wire and ran it through the eye of the lock a few times. It jammed when he tried to pull it back. He worked it back and forth and it snapped off inside. He drew the rest of it out and looked at it, worried. He hit the lock a few times to dislodge the small piece of wire it had taken. Nothing happened. Fuck it, he thought, it's a piece of wire in there so it takes their mind offa the key.

He stepped carefully into the store. Pale light from the front windows touched everything in his path. A dark blind covered the front door. He shook his head. There was no way he was going up front and trigger that bastard silent alarm. The store was large and clean.

147

Everything was in its place, the counters were bare alongside the cash register.

Don't be a jerk, he told himself.

Everything was along the back left wall and the rear counter like the fat man said. Stereos, record changers, receivers and speakers. He saw one tag. $899. Save $229.85.

Big deal, he thought.

The color portables were on the floor. Some of the TV screens were masked with paper signs. RCA 17″ diagonal Color. 19″ diagonal 100% Solid State Color TV. $399.73. Mfg. List Price $489.95.

Stop trying to add it up, he told himself. You get fucked, you get fucked. The hunnerd ain't bad.

He worked quickly. The portable color TVs went first. He stacked them to the side of the rear door. He resisted opening the door to look out. *Fuck it. They'll be there.*

He made several more trips with the stereos and record players and changers. There were cassette decks on the counter. The fat man hadn't mentioned cassette decks. *But shit, they're there on the counter. He said what's there, right?*

The stereo cassette decks were marked. Four-channel, 8-track cartridge deck, reg. $139.95. Sherm's Top Value $69.97.

"Sherm," he said. "Looks like you know how to make a buck."

He opened the rear door only when everything was ready. The night wind smelled fresh. It had stopped

148

raining. That's good, he thought. Now I won't ruin your goods, Sherm.

He worked fast and slipped in and out the door, setting everything outside. Before he went out the last time, he checked the back left wall section to see if he missed anything.

Looks good to me. Fuck the register. Come on.

Outside he took a quick breath and looked around from the shadows of the building. There was a small rear area enclosed by a fence for dumping boxes. The alley ran the length of the block behind the rear fence. There was a slat wood door with a hinge hook clasp. He flipped it off and began to set the goods outside the fence.

When he had it all done, he was breathing hard, but he didn't think it was from the work. Okay, he said to himself, now comes the tester. I think we made good time.

He lit a cigarette and stepped into the alley. He faced north, to his right, and puffed three times. Then he flipped the butt out in a high arc. Down the end of the alley, he heard an engine turn over.

A heavy refuse dump truck rumbled slowly down the alley. He watched from close inside the fence. The big metal box swung up and down, powered by the growling mechanism. Two men jumped off the truck. They began to load the goods inside. They got it all in quickly. The long metal arms raised again.

Jesus, that's neat, he thought. I never heard no dump truck for a heist. What asshole would even look?

149

The men jumped on the moving bin and put the goods down. The bin shifted back into place, covering the goods below. The men jumped off. The driver went behind the wheel. The second man went to the other side.

The dump truck rumbled down the alley. It cut right at the corner. He shook his head admiringly. He closed the wooden gate and leaned over and replaced the hasp hook.

His cigarette butt was still burning. He picked it up and took a few more puffs and flipped it away. He turned left at the corner and headed for the all-night movie.

I wonder what they got tonight? he thought.

19 He woke up feeling good. I'm rolling now, he thought. I'm onna way. A couple more jobs for Pete and I'll be okay.

He frowned at the date. McKeon would want to be hearing from him. *I don't want no job. I'll hafta give him some kinda song and dance. That fuckin' probation, it's a bummer.*

The old lady was still sleeping. He took a dollar from her purse and left the house. He walked the few blocks to the Greek's stand and ordered chili and eggs. The Greek looked at him. He put the dollar on the narrow counter.

"With some fries on it," he said, "and gimme coffee."

The Greek broke three eggs with one hand and sloshed them around. He shook the fries in the basket and spooned out the chili beans. The Greek didn't have much room to work around in. The outdoor stand wasn't more than ten feet across and had three stools off the counter. He pushed the mug of coffee across the dollar and left it. He got everything steaming hot on the plate and slid it over. He put two slices of bread down, picked up the dollar, and rang it up. He slapped the change down and turned to swab his grill.

Last time you see me, Greek, inna long time, he thought. He slipped the change into his pocket. He ate the plate clean and finished the coffee. He pushed the mug across and the Greek filled it again and pushed it back. He tapped his pockets and couldn't find a cigarette. The Greek watched him and put some oil on his grill and brushed it around.

"Hey, Greek, you gotta butt?"

The Greek reached into his shirt pocket and took a cigarette out of the pack and gave it to him. He nodded and lit up. He took a few puffs and belched. He finished the coffee and got off the stool.

The Greek picked up the plates and the coffee mug and dropped them into the bucket of sudsy water. He let some pale colored water out of the big coffee urn and added some coffee grounds on top. He threw the water into the sink. He picked up a peeled potato and began slicing it.

Owen watched the potato disappear. He flipped his hand and moved off. That fuckin' Greek, he thought, he must be nervous. He don't stop a fuckin' minute.

He still had a few hours to kill before he saw the fat man. Nobody was around. He walked across Alameda to Main. Traffic was heavy already on Main. He smelled the soot and exhaust all the way. He walked across the street and looked in Denny's windows. They had some pretty good threads but they were way too high. He turned his head. Sherm's front door was open. He saw people inside. No fuzz, no prowl cars.

Maybe they come down earlier, he thought. Sherm

152

wasn't going to fuck around. He had a business to run. Like the Greek, he thought, he don't waste no time.

He passed a sporting goods store. He looked over the scuba-diving equipment. Yeah, he thought, that'll be the day. The tennis rackets looked larger than he remembered. He rubbed the coins together in his pocket. That wasn't bad, he said to himself, remember? That Johnson, I wonder how he's doing.

He crossed the street at the next corner and walked to the alley. He looked inside the alley while he was moving. There was a black and white down the end. There were two big guys in plain-clothes talking with a cop wearing a white cap. He could see the wooden gate was open when he walked across. He could hear the car radio from the prowl car calling off signals.

It's a lotta crap, he wanted to tell them. You wanna know the truth, the real rip-off man is right there inside. That Sherm. He's way aheada you dumb bastards.

He went down Los Angeles Street and watched some of the guys in coveralls jockey cars into the small crowded parking lots. I can do that, he thought, it wouldn't be too bad. Unless you bang up some asshole's fender and then you're off looking again.

At Temple he turned north toward the Civic Center and the glittering glass and granite high rises. He saw the Criminal Courts buildings, people running in and out. Some looked worried, some didn't look anything.

Behind the buildings were the long curving concrete paths for pedestrian traffic and the long, cold white

153

stone benches overlooking the patches of grass. Across the mall were some bums stretched out asleep on the benches, warming in the sun. Some winos were down on the grass looking like crumpled rags.

He found a spot behind a thick bush sprouting tiny pink blossoms. He picked off a few and tasted them. They had a lemony tang. He chewed on them awhile, then brushed his teeth with them and spit them out. He looked and found a butt with two inches to go on it. He lay down on the soft grass and lit up and smoked. The sun warmed his bones and he felt soft and lazy. He looked up at the thin drifting trails of clouds in the pale blue sky. He watched them fall off and separate and disappear, and fell asleep.

He woke up to high-pitched giggles and laughter. A group of young girls came up the path pointing to a wino across the grass fighting off a fly in his sleep. The girls had long black hair and seemed to be dressed alike. They were the Little Tokyo girls from across Los Angeles Street along Pedro. Most of them were thin and didn't look bad.

He got up and walked out of the mall and went down Temple and bought a Coke for a dime at a stand. He picked a butt off an ashtray and lit up and moved away.

The long white El D was at the curb on Romaine in front of the phone booth. He saw the fat man behind the wheel and felt himself smiling when he walked over.

The car window was already rolled down. He said, "Hi, man, how you doing?" The fat man didn't say anything and he looked inside. The fat man was sitting there with his head against the high back-up seat. His arms hung stiffly at his sides. There was a round red bullet hole in the center of his forehead with a lot of black around the edges. His mouth was open but he didn't say anything.

The star sapphire and the gold ring were off his fingers, the thin pale gold wristwatch was gone from his wrist. The glove compartment lid was down. There wasn't anything inside it but space.

He walked around the other side of the car and saw all the blood staining the fat man's neck and white shirt. It made him feel sick and he backed off a step and looked away.

"For Christ sake," he said.

He heard a slight chattering sound as he came back to the sidewalk. The bluejay was teetering on a twig of the stubby hedge. It cocked its head toward him.

"The fat man caught it," he said to the bird. "We been fucked. There ain't gonna be no payoff today."

The bird chattered briefly.

"Yeah," he said to the jay, "I know. Tough shit."

He walked away wondering who ripped off the fat man.

20 McKeon sounded tired over the phone. "I'm glad you called, Kirby. I think maybe I've got a job lined up for you. You know anything about body repair work?"

"Shit, no. What's that?"

"That's what I figured," McKeon said. "You have a pencil? Write this down."

He looked at it again. "Earle's Body Shop?"

"It's worth a shot," McKeon said. "Earle's a decent guy. If he likes you, it could keep you out of trouble."

"Yeah. Thanks."

"How's it been going?" McKeon said.

"Well," he said. "You know."

McKeon sighed. "Yeah, Kirby. I know. We both know. And if you don't cut it with Earle, do us both a favor. Get back to me. Don't wait too long."

"Yeah. Okay."

The phone booth stank and was hot. He hung up and banged the box with his fist. His coin didn't drop out the bottom slot.

"You fucking box," he said. "Drop dead!"

The old lady was out of the house when he got there. He found some of the welfare money in the top drawer

156

of her dresser under some rolled-up thin stockings. He took two bills and some change from a compact on her dressing table.

The Greek was hosing down the pavement around the stand. Owen stepped over the hose and sat on the same end stool. The Greek finished the wetting down and put the hose down neatly in a coil. The Greek lifted the flap end of the counter and went inside the stand. He tapped the coffee urn for water and spilled it back over the top.

"How's my credit, Greek?" he said.

The Greek looked at him. He opened a big can of coffee and began spooning it into a tin measuring cup.

"I'll take a burger," he said.

The Greek poured the coffee from the measuring cup into the top of the urn. He reached up with a wooden ladle and stirred the grounds into the filter.

"No shit, Greek. And a cuppa coffee."

The Greek put a cover over the can of coffee and put it under the counter. He went to the sink and took a potato out of the water. He shook the water off and began to slice it.

"Okay, Greek." He took one of the bills out of his pocket and put it down on the counter. He kept his hand on it and slapped it a few times. The Greek kept slicing potatoes. He pushed the bill across the counter. "With onions, Greek," he said.

The Greek rolled the sliced potatoes in a towel and then dumped them into the wire basket. He opened the refrigerator and took a hamburger patty out. He heated up his grill and sloshed some oil around with his brush and slapped the patty on. He reached under the counter and got an onion out of a bin. He picked up a knife and scraped off the skin and began to slice the onion.

"Hey, Greek," he said, "how come you never cry when you slice up an onion? I swear I never once seen you cry."

The Greek looked at him. His eyes were large and dark and sad. "What good is for to cry?" he said. He scooped up the sliced onion and threw it on the grill. He flattened the patty with a board and turned it over. The patty sizzled. He turned the onion rings over. The fumes caught Owen's eyes.

"Jesus," he said, "how the fuck you do it?"

The Greek drew a mug of coffee from the urn and set it in front of him. He pushed the sugar bowl over. There was a small bowl of chili relish and mustard and ketchup and he got them together and pushed them over. He put a roll on the grill.

"I cry one time," the Greek said. He leaned over the counter. His white hands were spread apart. His black eyes were burning. "When Santos, my boy, was killed. After that, I no cry. I no cry for some goddamn onion."

"Yeah, Greek, I heard about it," he said. "But that wasn't me, you know, not my friends. That was some fuckin' gang from over the Heights. That's how they do here."

The Greek stared at him. He turned and spit on the wood slatting of his floor and rubbed it with his foot. He picked up a spatula and turned the roll over. He picked up the patty and the onions and slapped them on the hot roll. He slid the roll off onto a plate and set it in front of him.

"Eat," he said.

He began to put the relish and mustard and ketchup over the burger. The Greek was wiping off the grill. It had a good smell of hamburger and fried onions.

The Greek looked at his hand. He moved it away and the Greek picked his bill off and dropped it in the box and rang it up. He got some change and slapped it down on the counter.

"How old was Santos, Greek?" he said. "I mean, at the time?"

"He was before twelve," the Greek said. "He was two weeks before twelve."

"Well, I'm sorry, Greek. No shit, I'm real sorry."

The Greek put away the rest of the onion in a piece of plastic paper. He shook his head. "Is no good here. Is no good place. Everybody steal, they hit, they kill. For what? You tell me, for what?"

He had the hamburger in his mouth. It tasted the way he wanted it. He spoke with his mouth full. "Beats me, Greek. It's how they do. Shit, I didn't start it."

He finished and bummed another cigarette off the Greek. Then he got off the stool and started the long walk over to Earle's.

Earle's Body Shop Repair was on a corner lot east of the freeway. It was in a run-down neighborhood with small trucking concerns and moving and storage buildings. There was a mission on the next corner and a machinist's shop, a narrow coffee shop, a store featuring plumbing supplies.

He came on the lot tired from the walk. Noise from the freeway hammered the air. From an open tin-roofed shed there was more hammering. He saw a man working over a dusty car. A battered white tow truck was parked at the side. Cars stood all around, dented, ripped, new and old, some nearly totaled. He saw sprung trunks, shattered windshields, bashed-in radiators.

Another man in coveralls made a hissing sound. He was spraying a thin mist of paint from a nozzle attached to a can over a red convertible Healey.

Shit, that don't look hard, he thought.

He found Earle talking on the phone in a small office at the other end of the lot. Earle was behind a small desk covered by a clutter of order forms, bills and supply catalogs. Earle had one leg up on the desk. "Yeah, yeah," Earle was saying, "only stop the bullshit already and take care of it. It ain't no big deal, I'm asking thirty-six bucks for the paint and fender. Your guy was here, he okayed it, so where the fuck's the money?"

Earle saw him come in and winked. He listened and nodded his head. "Yeah, yeah, you told me that a dozen times already. Just send me the check and stop fuckin' me around."

He lit the cigarette in his mouth. He looked at Owen. "You wanna know something? I speak to one more asshole today and I go over the wall. Now what's your problem?"

160

"McKeon, Mr. McKeon, he sent me. You Earle?"

"Yeah, that's me. Mac sent you, huh? Oh, yeah, you're the kid he tole me about. What's your name?"

"Kirby. Owen Kirby."

Earle scratched his leg. "Yeah, that's it. You need a job, he said, right?"

"Yeah. The only trouble is I don't know nothin' about no body work."

Earle shrugged and took a deep puff and stubbed out the cigarette. "It ain't much to learn. It ain't no picnic, don't misunderstand me. Sometimes you gotta bust your balls. But if you wanna job, and you wanna put out a little, you got it. Okay?"

"Sure," he said, "but what if—"

Earle got up. "Come on. Let's take a walk outside. I'll show you around."

Earle came around the desk. He limped badly on one leg. Earle noticed his look. Outside he said, "Don't worry. I didn't get this onna job. I wanted to be a race driver once. I thought I was some kinda hotshot. My first race, second lap, I spun into the wall. Totaled the car. They nearly hadda cut off my goddamn foot. So now I'm grounded. The worst happens to me I get to speak to a lotta assholes onna phone."

Earle pointed to the cars waiting care. There was a tan late model Mercedes 450 SL, its side gouged, headlights torn out. A yellow Firebird next to it was nearly new, too. The hood and radiator were smashed back, the windshield shattered.

Earle waved to the distance. "We get 'em right offa

161

the freeway. It's a good place for business. The assholes out there are inna war, day and night. We drag 'em off and if they're still alive, we get to fix up the wrecks."

Owen shook his head at the Firebird. "Y'mean, you can put that together so she'll run?"

"We only do the body work, remember," Earle said. "To get the sonofabitch to run, the guy's gotta find a mechanic. I know a couple guys, in case."

Owen walked around the tan Mercedes. He shook his head at the damaged side. "Yeah, but even so. This here sideswipe job. How you straighten that out?"

Earle stooped and picked up a long wooden mallet. "You start with this. It's dented in, you work inside, you dent it out. Okay?"

He stared and felt the weight. Earle had given him the mallet. "Well, yeah, but—"

Earle was moving away. "Pick any one you want."

He went after the limping man. "Hey, Earle, wait—"

Earle stopped. "What's the problem?"

"Well, man, like I told you, I never did none of this. Some of these mothers, they're like new. What if I was to ruin something?"

Earle rubbed his jaw. He needed a shave. There was grime and grease on his face and arms. "Maybe they was new, but now they ain't, now they're wrecks, right? So how can you hurt a wreck?"

"Well, yeah, but shit, Earle, say I do something wrong by accident?" He hefted the mallet. It was heavy.

162

Earle looked him in the eyes. "So we fix it up. This here is a body-repair joint, ain't it?"

"Well, yeah, only I don't wanna fuck up my first day."

Earle lit another cigarette. "I'll tell you something, kid. I come from Philly, South Philly, and we didn't have shit. My old man died and I didn't have no school. My old lady died and for a while the sisters took care a me. I got out and farted around, this and that, and then I got the war.

"After the war, I figured I had Philly, fuck it, so I come out here. When I opened this place, I didn't know a thing, not a goddamn thing, nothing. But I needed a job and money, and I got so busy hammering cars back in shape, I never had time to worry about what I din't know.

"Now Mac tells me you need the job. I don't know what you done, and I don't give a shit. That's between you and Mac. You want the job, I'm saying it's yours. If it don't work out, it don't work out. So you give it a whirl. It'll keep your nose clean. What'cha got to lose?"

He bobbed his head. He liked Earle. He swung the big mallet. "Okay. I warned ya, so you won't get sore if I bust up one a those ten-grand jobs."

Earle smiled. "Okay, okay, you warned me." He pointed toward the shed. "You can watch Joe and Harry, maybe pick up some know-how. You keep your eyes open and you learn. You want to tackle something, you think you can handle it, you do it. If you

163

get stuck, the bastard won't come around, you ask. If they're too busy, you ask me. If I don't know, we're all in trouble."

Owen took a step away. "Okay, Earle."

Earle said, "If we're all too busy, you sit down and have yourself a Coke. You get the blowtorch sometimes, and you play with it on some a the old heaps. See how you do matching up colors. Maybe you're good at that, who knows?"

Owen hesitated. "You paying me for practicing?"

Earle laughed. His teeth were white but crooked. "Not for long, I hope. We'll have you sweatin' your butt off soon enough."

Owen looked into the distance and thought about the fat man sitting behind the wheel of the big white El D with the bullet in his head and blood down the side of his face and neck.

I done a pretty good job for him and I get stiffed.

He pointed to the tan Mercedes 450. "I'll try that mother. I never been this close to one before."

"She's all yours," Earle said. He limped back to the office.

You an okay cat, Earle, he thought, you know that? Even with that gimpy foot. You know, I got a good mind to do good here.

21 He got through the week. He left the house early and had coffee at Jack's Cafe across the street from the body shop. He couldn't wait to get at the tan Mercedes. The creamed driver's side came around slowly. Earle looked and said, "Okay, you're doin' okay," and walked off with that jerky twisting limp.

When it came to the headlights, he was surprised to find some of the things he had learned at Camp Sawyer came to mind and worked. He connected and taped the wires and put in the small bulbs. He picked up the headlight lamps and began tapping the shield over them.

Earle said, "That ain't bad. Where'd you get the parts?"

He looked up. "Oh, I found them, Earle."

"Yeah. Where'd you find them?"

He put down the small mallet. "Oh, you know, Earle. Around."

Earle blew smoke. "You mean, you lifted them."

"Well, yeah. I seen this other Mercedes in a lot. Same model. So I figured it would fit."

"Jesus," Earle said. "You trying to do, bring the cops

165

down here? Jesus, business ain't that bad." Earle leaned and tapped his shoulder. "I mean it, kid, no more a that shit. We need parts, we buy 'em. Sometimes we make 'em on what's around. But you don't walk no streets and grab, understand?"

"Okay, Earle. You want me to take 'em off and put 'em back?"

Earle pushed the back of his head roughly. "Up your ass, Charlie."

Later Earle whistled him into his office. He showed him the green metal box with the petty cash. He showed him the supply catalogs and the list of metal shops in the area.

"Okay?" Earle said.

They took him off the Mercedes and gave him the Firebird. He did a bumper job on a Monte Carlo, put a door handle on a Chevy, got a sprung trunk lid back on a silver Porsche.

Earle sent him off to pick up some paint. He counted out the money carefully from the cash box. He felt hot and uncomfortable alone in Earle's office with the money there.

That Earle, he's a fuckin' freak trusting me this way.

He longed to do a job with the tow truck. "Sure," Earle said. "When you can get your driver's license. That's what, next year? Okay, that ain't too long."

Jesus, he thought, here's Earle talking about next year. Maybe I'm doing okay. Hey, how about that?

Joe and Harry got him on the spray gun. It was nothing, he thought, a breeze.

166

Harry tapped him. "Only the hood, dummy, not the windshield."

The glass sparkled deep blue.

"Oh, for Christ sake! Shit."

"Next time you mask it."

The refrigerated drive-in wagon came around three times a day. Coffee, Coke, sandwiches. He bolted his down and went back to waxing and buffing the polish.

Earle called him in. He handed him a small envelope. "Payday, Kirby. You better count it now. I wanna know you think it's fair."

He shook his head, feeling warm. He slipped the little Manila envelope inside his jeans. "It's okay," he said. "I know I still ain't much good. Whatever you gimme, it's okay, Earle."

"Bullshit," Earle said. "Nobody is any good first fuckin' week. You count it anyway."

Earle waited. *Well, shit.* He ripped the envelope and saw crisp bills. He looked at Earle. Earle lit a cigarette and blew smoke. "Come on, for Christ sake," Earle said, "will you count the fuckin' money?"

His fingers were stiff. "I got fifty-five here plus some change."

Earle didn't blink. "Change is money, too. How much change?"

He made it eighty-two cents.

"Okay," Earle said, "now you know what your rate is."

"What rate?"

"You get two and a quarter an hour. I have to hold out some for tax."

167

He shoved the money back in his pocket. He felt very good. He couldn't remember when he ever felt this good.

"Whatever you say, Earle. No shit. Next week, honest to Christ, I'll do better. Maybe I'll be worth the dough."

Earle scratched his leg. "That's okay by me. When you do that, once you ain't no apprentice, your rate goes to two anna half."

"How come?"

"It's the law," Earle said. "Minimum fucking wage."

"No shit," he said.

Earle came by later. "Okay. Wash up and take off."

He looked around. Earle was smiling. "Hey, what'cha mean, man? It ain't time."

"So what?" Earle said. "First paycheck. I'm givin' ya time to celebrate."

"Aw, come on, Earle. That ain't—"

Earle said, "Get your ass outta here. Come on. I ain't no fuckin' slave driver. Put down the fuckin' brush, relax. The heap ain't goin' no place."

Joe and Harry were grinning like two fucking cats, he thought, when he waved. *I don't believe this, it ain't real.*

He walked in a happy daze. He was heading south, downtown, his hand brushing the money in his pocket. He could feel the crisp new bills. Three tens, four fives, five singles. Plus the change, he told himself, don't forget the fucking change. He laughed.

It was an hour before the evening rush hour. Shoppers crowded the walk, hurrying to get it all in and go home. More cars came out of the parking lots and filled

168

the wide streets. He bumped into people. He didn't get mad at anybody. He felt too good inside.

He passed a sporting goods store and came back. He looked at the equipment. Bats and balls, cleat shoes, the scuba gear, Puma and Adidas track shoes, snappily two-toned. There were wood and metal tennis rackets. Cans of balls.

His hand rubbed the new money in his jeans. Shit, why not? he asked himself. *Stealin's out now, you are goin' straight.*

Maybe if he bought a racket, he could get Charley and the guys to play. They could go over to the courts in the city park. He could show them what Johnson showed him. It could be kicks, give them something to do.

His eyes narrowed and he pursed his lips at the metal racket. I wonder what they get for that mother? he thought. I bet that Johnson, he would really faint, see me with that metal racket.

He looked closely. He couldn't make out any price for the rackets. People brushed past behind him. He stared at the two-pronged aluminum handle above the black leather grip.

Stamped in black and silver letters inside the groove in the metal was the word Master. Shit, he thought, if that ain't neat!

A blue racked cover with white trim at the sides and white letters stamped on it said Head. There was some kind of a design over the white letters, a bent white stripe and under it a small white ball.

He hesitated. *Shit, I buy this for a week's pay, I'll be*

busted till next Friday. That bastard looks like it costs.

He backed away, his eyes dwelling on the Head racket. Maybe next week, he said to the racket. He didn't notice the chopped-down sedan that slid in close to the curb. He heard the sudden rush of feet too late.

Something hard thudded against the back of his head. His eyes spun. His vision fragmented. Then things came together and he saw a woman looking at him with her mouth open. "What the fuck?" he thought angrily, and then he was hit from behind again. The woman started to scream and jump up and down in one place. The sidewalk buckled under him.

His head hurt and he staggered to the side. He still didn't know what happened. Something lashed at the side of his face. It stung and hurt and he turned, off-balance, and saw them. His eyes blurred from the blows, but he saw.

Small glossy-haired figures were all around him. There were so many, he couldn't count them. He balled his fists and they danced away. Something hit him on the back of his neck and seemed to glance up to the base of his skull. There was a roaring sound in his ears. The sidewalk spun away.

He swayed on his knees. He saw the legs and feet of people standing. He saw something black flashing toward him. He put up his arm too late as the boot crashed into his side.

There goes your rib, get up, you fuckin' jerk! he screamed at himself.

Somehow he staggered to his feet and wobbled backward. His back hit a wall. His eyes rolled and he saw the alley. His legs were numb, he couldn't get them to move.

Come on, you bastards, move for Crissakes! What's wrong?

Nothing happened. He raged inwardly. *You mothers!*

They came at him with a swift rush. They were small, swarthy-skinned, with black glittering eyes. They wore their hair high, oiled and brushed back smoothly. They wore tight tan chinos and plaid Pendleton shirts flapping outside their pants. Their highly polished black boots had very thick heels.

He recognized them now. The Chicano gang from the east side of his neighborhood. Carmona's old gang. *The Piratas!*

He pushed himself off the wall and swung as they came into focus. He thought he hit something but they swarmed over him like ants. They moved fast from all sides, swinging hard things he couldn't see that made him gasp and wince.

My blade, he thought, where the fuck is my blade?

He bounced off the wall and tumbled into the alley. They knocked him to his knees. He heard a ripping sound. Fire laced his arm. He was getting up when they jumped him and flattened him, face down. Dimly he heard people shouting.

He felt his pockets ripped, and he rolled over. He swung and caught somebody. His blow felt weak, in slow motion. A brown hand came down and smashed

171

against his face. He saw a thin, drizzling, red mist.

Suddenly he felt them leave him. He heard running feet. Voices shouting.

Too late, people, he said silently. You shoulda done something before them little bastards killed me.

He spit blood and sat up. His face felt swollen and lopsided. His right eye twitched. He put his hand up to quiet the jumping nerve. His hand came down crimson.

He looked down and saw his slashed pants pockets. He didn't have to put his hand in to know, but he did anyway.

Fuckin' bastards took it all. My first fuckin' payday.

He got to his feet, reeling. A man stepped close, peering. "You okay, kid? Hold on, I think there's an ambulance coming."

He dimly heard the siren approaching. Yeah, he thought, I can use it. Then he remembered what happened after his last alley fight.

Fuck it, he thought.

People stepped back as if frightened by his appearance. They tried to stop him with soft, cautious words.

He kept on walking.

I got to make it home, he told himself. Then I got to find those li'l bastards and get even.

22 He had strips of white
tape over him. They were in the park. It was early.

"Shit," Charley said, "them little bastards wasn't the
Piratas."

"The shit they wasn't," he said. "I seen them, I told
you—"

"Yeah, but you said how little they was. That's the
little kid gang, the eight to eleven li'l bastards, that's
the *chiquillos*."

He stared. "Them little bastards was eight to eleven
years old what ripped me off?"

Charley shrugged. "Shit, man, they're wild. They're
like a packa wild dogs. It don't mean a fuck how old
them li'l bastards are, they can mess you."

He touched his face. "Yeah. I already know that.
But they're part of the Piratas, ain't they? I mean, shit,
they dress the same, they're from the same neighborhood."

Jerry broke in. "I hear they run their own way. They
ain't got no leader. They just do what the fuck they
want. They all wanna do good so later the gang, the
Piratas, takes them in."

Owen glowered. He hurt and ached all over. Know-

173

ing little kids did it to him made it hurt more. He knew most street gangs had young offshoot members, but that didn't make him feel any better.

"First I'm jumped by these three dudes in that alley. Then I get them five assholes, them fuckin' Mongols, that don't know nothin', and they rip me off, and now this, these—what you say they was called?"

"Chiquillos," Charley said.

"Yeah. That makes three in a row I been hit."

"Yeah, man," Nick said, "but you gotta remember, like every time they had you by the balls, by the numbers. You had the three on you, then the three with the two back-ups, the shotgun and all, and now you got these li'l bastards—how many you say there was?"

He wagged his head. "Shit, there was so many, I couldn't even count 'em. Maybe ten, twelve—shit, there was a lot of them li'l bastards."

"Well," Nick said, "that's what I mean, man. What can ya do, all them bastards on you?"

"What I can do," he said, "what I really like to do now, is get in some gang and beat the shit outta them —them li'l bastards."

"Yeah," Charley said, "only you can't do that unless you was to go in with some kid gang. How you gonna do that?"

He thought about it. Charley was right. He'd look like an asshole going around jumping little kids.

He punched his hands together. It put a stitch in his side and he had to wait and catch his breath. He rubbed his sore rib. "Well," he said angrily, "I'm really

thinking about some gang. This shit has got to stop
flying my way."

"There ain't nothing around here," Jerry said. "Only
the Piratas which is Chicano, and the Pharaohs and
Sinners, which is bloods. The Nomads, they're bloods,
too. So what you got?"

He stared at his hands. "I got shit, that's what."

Charley said, "You know, we can do a gang. We got
enough right here for a starter."

"Us?" Owen said. "There's only the four of us."

Charley shrugged. "So you was ripped off by them
Mongols, right? What they have, only five, right?"

"Yeah, but they had the car, remember. They also
had the shotgun, that kid inna back."

"No problem," Charley said. "Jerry can always find
us a car, right, Jerry?"

Jerry smiled. "No problem."

He remembered how good Jerry was at jumping the
wires on cars, and lifting them. Jerry had stolen more
cars, before he got into drugs, than anybody he knew.

"We need something like the shotgun. That mother
will scare the piss outta anybody."

"We got that and more," Charley said. "I got a
Remington M 1100. It's a semi-automatic 3-shot. I also
got a Colt .25 automatic and a .22 Astra automatic and
five boxes ammo."

Owen looked at Charley. "When you get those?"

"While you was away. We lifted them for some dude,
but he never showed up to pay off. So we got 'em."

Jerry laughed. "Tell him about the grenades."

175

He looked at Charley.

"That's no crap," Charley said. "We got grenades, too. We got a box, six of the mothers."

"How you get grenades, for Christ sake?"

Charley shrugged. "Same deal. Some dude come outta the army. We coulda picked up a bazooka, too, only that mother was too big to carry."

He spat. "Jesus," he said.

"We could call us The Four," Nick said.

"The four what?"

"Just The Four," Nick said. "There's just the four of us."

"Shit," he said, "what kinda name is that? It don't mean nothing."

"Well, what the fuck Mongols mean?" Nick said. "That don't mean nothin', neither. You said you seen it on the bumper."

"That's what it said," he said. "It said Mongols, all right."

"What about Nomads," Nick said. "Nomads don't mean nothin', neither."

"Well, there's Pharaohs," he said. "That means something." He thought. "Sinners. That means something. But then there's Tips." He shook his head. "What the fuck is Tips mean?"

"Piratas," Nick said. "How about them?"

"That means Pirates," he told Nick. "This kid Carmona told me."

Nick shrugged. "Okay, so what? That don't mean The Four don't mean somethin'. It means us." He moved his finger to each of them. "One, two, three, four. You get it?"

He looked at Charley. "I don't mind, Charley. What you think?"

Charley nodded. "The Four ain't bad." He said it over a few times. "I dig it, you know? It sounds, like mysterious."

"Yeah," he said, "inna way." He looked at Charley. "You sure you wanna get into this?"

Charley yawned. "Well, shit, we can start it, see how we do. Tell you the truth, I don't dig gangs too much. Look at all the time you waste. I can be out makin' out, doing deals. But maybe we oughtta. No reason the other dudes can cut it and we can't."

He looked at Charley. Charley would want to be headman. Charley Bee was the one with the brains there. Charley could figure any deal. Charley was smarter than shit, he knew.

"You can be headman," Charley said to him.

He looked at Jerry and Nick.

"Okay with me," Jerry said.

"Yeah, good deal," Nick said. "You're the best fighter here. I can't fight worth shit."

Owen rubbed his rib. "Well, okay," he said. "But let's forget them grenades for now, huh? I don't trust them mothers."

23

He couldn't sleep that night. His body hurt but his mind roamed.

Headman.

We start off easy, he said to himself. We do it cool. We take our time and look around. There's lotsa ways we can make out. We don't hassle nobody big, we don't get our ass in a sling right off. We play it cool.

He wondered how many men Justin Dye had when he started. *Maybe he only had a couple, three or four, too, when he started. Then he started to build up, put it together. There's others we can pull in when we get going and they see we can protect them. Lotsa cats on the street afraid to move around. So we let 'em see The Four is okay, we do good, we stand by.*

Them fucking grenades, he thought, I don't want no part of that. Jesus, we drop one a those and we really hurt somebody. Shit, no, we got enough, that other stuff Charley's got.

That jerk Hawkins. Someday maybe The Four will drop around, give him a little blast, shake the dumb bastard up.

Hawkins was running away, pleading for his life, when he fell asleep.

178

Owen's face was still swollen when he woke up. The cuts were healing. His body was still sore from the beating and stomping.

Them goddamn li'l bastards, don't think I wouldn't want to pay them off, too.

He took another bill out of his mother's purse. Maybe that car Jerry comes up with won't have the gas, he thought. I guess I got to thinka those things.

The Greek's stand was closed. What the fuck? he thought. It ain't Sunday, it's Saturday. He oughtta be here for the business.

He found a bread truck and then a milk truck. He threw the rest of the milk and eggs away. Goddamn Greek, he thought, I felt like some chili.

He walked around wondering which end of town would be a good place to start. *No school today, so we can't rip off no lunch money.*

He looked over a little outdoor taco stand. We could meet here, he thought, it ain't too bad. The Greek's would be better, only he ain't got no outdoor tables. Maybe I can talk to him about that.

He remembered Santos. *Shit, no, he wouldn't go for that. Not the Greek. Man, he would spit all over us. He don't dig no gangs. Okay, fuck him. There's other places.*

He walked around, checked a few spots. All the gangs had outdoor meeting places. Drive-ins, eating places. They took over all the tables when they came in. Nobody argued.

We can meet in the park meanwhile, he thought, till we find us a spot.

179

He hoped the other guys wouldn't be disappointed if he hadn't come up with a good meeting place yet. They might start thinking he wasn't such a fucking good headman after all.

There were a lot of places but they weren't safe. The big gangs dropped in at different times, cruising the neighborhood.

We don't want no hassles yet, he told himself. I'll have to explain that to the guys. Four ain't too many to work with. I got to see we ain't suckered in nowhere.

A little after noon, he was heading for the same place in the park. A car honked behind him as he was crossing the street. He turned crossly.

Jerry sat behind the wheel of a Chevy Camaro. It wasn't more than two years old. Charley and Nick sat in the back seat.

He leaned into the open window. "Jesus, you jumped this?"

Jerry shook his head. He showed him the keys in the ignition. "You wait long enough at the post office, you do good. The assholes leave the motors going while they jump inside, mail a letter. They ain't allowed to park long."

He backed off, admiring the black and yellow Camaro. "Hey, what about the plates?" he said.

Charley smiled. "We switched them. These come off a Buick Apollo at the supermarket."

He opened the door. "Hey, neat-o." He looked at Charley. "You got the pea-popper?"

Charley lifted the long shotgun. He took a 3-inch

shell out of his pocket and held it between his fingers.

"Jesus, that what they shoot?"

Charley tapped the stock. "This is good for hunting, too. You know, ducks, deer, shit like that."

He sat down on the front seat alongside Jerry and pulled the door shut. Charley tapped him. He turned. Charley put something over his shoulder.

"That's the Colt automatic," Charley said. "Nick's got the Astra .22 caliber. Okay?"

He nodded. He looked at the blue-steel Colt. It looked new. It felt snug in his hand. He pressed the release and the clip dropped into his hand. He counted the rounds. It was a six-shot magazine.

"Yours loaded?" he said to Nick.

Nick held up his self-loader. "Yeah. Charley put in the clip."

"Okay," he said. He turned to Jerry. "We got gas?"

Jerry pointed to the gauge. "Nearly full."

"Let's go," he said.

The Camaro slid off. Jerry handled it with his fingertips. "Power steering," Jerry said. "Neat?"

Owen circled thumb and middle finger. "Neat-o."

Jerry turned the corner. "She's an eight," he said. "A fuckin' bomb. Watch." The Camaro leaped. It roared down the street. The light ahead blinked to yellow. Jerry looked at him. The light was red at the corner when he touched it. The tires grabbed. The Camaro stopped short.

"Power brakes," Jerry said.

"Jesus," he said. "She's a fuckin' bomb."

181

Jerry laughed. The car purred smoothly ahead when the light changed. "She's loaded. Get this." He moved a dial on the dash. Something whirred. It whirred at a higher pitch. Cool air flowed over them. "Fuckin' air condition."

"Man," he said.

Jerry laughed. "Get this." He hit a button. Music came. Jerry laughed. He moved a dial. The music came fuller. "Fuckin' AM/FM stereo," Jerry said. He pressed a side button. The front windows rolled down. He hit one more. The rear windows rolled down. The air rushed through. Jerry laughed. He hit the buttons again and the windows went rolling up quietly. "Fuckin' power windows," he said.

He thought of the fat man. He wondered how they got him to roll down his windows. Probably one on each side, he thought. With a gun on him.

He said aloud, "This here's some wagon, Jer. You really honest to Christ got us some wagon."

They drove around. Coming into the next corner, Jerry drove it hard and then braked as he turned in. The tires grabbed. The rear end came around. Jerry got it straight.

"Well," he said. "She oversteers a little."

Jerry picked up the freeway on-ramp. He took the freeway doing fifty and let it out. The motor roared. The landscape blurred.

"We better watch it, Jer," he said. "Fuckin' patrols out there clockin'. They stop us, we're dead."

Jerry took his foot off. He cut into the inside lane

and went down the next off-ramp. "Well," he said, "I only wanted to show you. She's some fuckin' bomb, right?"

He wagged his head. "Man, you ain't shittin'." He spoke over his shoulder. "We got to watch it, Charley, right?"

"You're headman," Charley said. "You're calling it."

He settled back. "Well, yeah," he said.

Jerry drove. He went three blocks and turned right at the light. He went right again at the next light. He took another right turn at the next red. "Here we are," he said.

He flapped his hand. "Just cruise it awhile. Up and down. We're only lookin'."

Jerry turned left. He moved his hand up and down. Jerry slowed. The Camaro moved. He reached out and cut the radio. Without the music, the air conditioner made noise. He hit the dash button and killed it.

He spoke over his shoulder. "We gotta watch it, Charley, right?"

"You're calling it," Charley said. "You're the headman."

He sniffed. "Well," he said. "I think we oughtta play it cool awhile, you know? We don't want to get busted first shot out doing The Four."

Nick was working his safety. He clicked it on and off.

"You better put that away, Nick," he said. "We get pulled over, what happens?"

"Hey, yeah," Nick said. "You're fuckin' right, Owe." He put the .22 down between his legs.

183

"Charley," he said, "you got something for this stuff? You got a bag or something?"

"Sure," Charley said. "I got this laundry."

He watched Charley open the big laundry bag at his feet. Charley put the Remington in. Charley held out his hand and Nick gave him the .22 and Charley checked the safety and put it in the bag. He reached into his pocket and took out the Colt and handed it over the seat to Charley.

Charley said, "You had your safety off."

"Yeah," he said. "I know."

Charley put the Colt in with the others. He folded the bag around and pushed it down behind the front seats.

"That's good, Charley," he said. "I think that's better, right?"

"No sweat," Charley said. "You're calling it."

Jerry drove south out of their neighborhood. The tough Chicano gangs would be just up ahead. The Camaro glided across, beating the red light.

"Hold it," he said.

The tires grabbed. The Camaro bit and lurched. Jerry looked at him.

He pointed to a car at the curb ahead. It was a T-Bird, black, maybe ten years old. "Take a look," he said.

A small piece of cardboard hung from the rear bumper, almost covering the plate.

"Hey," Charley said. "That the one? It says Mongols."

Owen moved his hand to Jerry. "Pull up," he said.

The Camaro eased up alongside. The T-Bird was empty.

"That drive-in," Nick said. "Maybe they're in there."

"Go up slow," he told Jerry.

The Camaro crept. The sign said Al's Oasis. It was a small taco and burger stand set at the far end of the corner lot. There were five white-topped round tables and plastic chairs. Three tables were open. A Mexican couple and two kids sat at the far one. A light-haired kid sat alone at the near one. There was a thin line at the counter window. He looked hard and couldn't make out the other four.

Fuckin' corkscrew, he thought.

He opened his car door. He spoke over his shoulder. "Cover me."

Jerry said, "Hey, don't you want your twenny-five?"

He grimaced. "I don' need it for this motherfucker. The other fuckin' Mongols, they ain't here."

He walked into the lot. The kid drank his Coke. He had some fries left on a paper plate.

He tapped the kid's shoulder from behind. "Hey, motherfucker, you still carry your corkscrew?"

The kid turned. He looked up. "I don't know you. Buzz off."

The kid turned back to his Coke. Owen tapped him harder on the shoulder. The kid was thin. "Turn around, motherfucker, you know me."

The kid turned.

"You ripped me off a week ago, motherfucker," he said to the kid. "There was five of you. The driver and the asshole inna back with the shotgun. Your buddy had the switchblade knife. The other creep had the beer-can opener. You had the fuckin' corkscrew."

185

The kid looked pale. "Now, hey, look," he said.

"Don't give me 'hey, look,' motherfucker. On your feet."

The kid hesitated. He looked at the Mexican couple and the kids. He moved his feet slowly, almost one at a time.

Owen moved his thumb. "Up," he said. "I wanna see that fuckin' corkscrew now without the shotgun on my back."

The kid's hand came up. Silver glinted. His hand jerked. There was a snapping noise. Something very hot burned into Owen's belly. Suddenly he couldn't stand.

What the fuck? he thought.

His knees slid on the ground. He looked down at his hands. They were pressed close together. Blood leaked through. He couldn't believe that was his blood staining his fingers red.

Hey, man, what's happening?

The light-haired kid sat. Somebody shouted. He was falling. There was no way he could keep from falling over. The sky seemed to be racing away. Hey, don't do that, he wanted to say. You're making me dizzy.

He watched the sky go up and up and then he couldn't see the sky at all. Man, he thought, that sky now is really outta sight.

His mouth opened. His lips moved. He wanted to say something. He couldn't find the words.

What the fuck? he thought, what the fuck?